D1192651

ATOMIC ABSORPTION SPECTROPHOTOMETRY

After a brief historical outline of the measurement of atomic absorption spectra the basic theory involved is presented and such important conceptions as the atomic absorption coefficient and oscillator strength are derived and explained. The implications of the Beer-Lambert Law for heterochromatic radiation measurement on the analytical curves are briefly discussed.

The different techniques of producing the absorption medium with free atoms are described and the one most frequently used, i.e. the flame, is dealt with in some detail. The important properties of the light sources (hollow cathode lamps, vapour discharge tubes, radiofrequency electrodeless discharge tubes) used in atomic absorption spectrophotometry are mentioned and a brief instruction is given for the laboratory manufacture of hollow cathode lamps. After a brief description of the different means for the isolation and detection of radiation used in atomic absorption spectrophotometry, the critical factors determining sensitivity and precision are discussed together with the different equipment available commercially.

In the second part of the book instructions for analytical work are given. First some generally valid principles on the optimum working conditions, on the preparation of standard solutions etc. are presented, followed by detailed information on the analytical possibilities of determination and the procedures used by different workers in this field. The elements are divided according to their properties from the atomic absorption point of view into six groups: the alkali metals, the alkaline earth metals, nonferrous metals, ferrous metals, noble metals and the rest.

The text ends with a list of analytical lines for all elements so far measured together with their oscillator strengths and the sensitivities reported in different flames (acetylene-air, acetylene-nitrous oxide, acetylene-oxygen).

This book should be of great interest to those working in analytical laboratories and to university students reading chemistry and/or physics.

188 pages, including 28 illustrations.

Ph.D. in 1964.

Both authors have co-published several papers in various international journals. Their interest has been aimed especially at problems of the atomic absorption analysis of inorganic materials, interference effects and their interpretation and measurement with absorption tubes.

ATOMIC ABSORPTION
SPECTROPHOTOMETRY

INTERNATIONAL SERIES OF PHYSICAL ANALYSIS

ATOMIC ABSORPTION SPECTROPHOTOMETRY

IVAN RUBESKA
BEDRICH MOLDAN

ENGLISH TRANSLATION EDITED BY
P. T. WOODS, B.A. (CANTAB.), D.PHIL.
DIVISION OF QUANTUM METROLOGY
NATIONAL PHYSICAL LABORATORY

CRC PRESS

A DIVISION OF
THE **CHEMICAL RUBBER** CO.
CLEVELAND, OHIO

INTERNATIONAL SCIENTIFIC SERIES

139211   NORTHWEST MISSOURI STATE
UNIVERSITY LIBRARY
MARYVILLE, MISSOURI 64468

Published in the U.S.A. by
The Chemical Rubber Co.,
18901 Cranwood Parkway, Cleveland, Ohio 44128

© Ivan Rubeška and Bedřich Moldan, 1967
Translated by Ivan Rubeška, 1968
English edition first published in 1969 by
Iliife Books, an imprint of the Butterworth Group, in co-edition with
SNTL – Publishers of Technical Literature,
Prague

Second Impression 1971

© Butterworths, 1969

Library of Congress Catalog Card Number 74–81279

Printed by photo-lithography and made in Great Britain at
The Pitman Press, Bath

543.085
R 89a

CONTENTS

Foreword   7

The history of measurement of atomic absorption spectra   9

CHAPTER 1   The absorption of radiation by free atoms   13
            1.1 Oscillator strength   13
            1.2 Atomic absorption coefficient   15
            1.3 Line profiles   17
            1.4 The Beer-Lambert Law   21
            1.5 The relation between absorbance and concentration of atoms   22
            1.6 Thermal excitation   26
            1.7 Atomic resonance fluorescence   27

CHAPTER 2   Absorption media   29
            2.1 The flame   30
            2.2 Flame mixtures used in absorption flame photometry   30
            2.3 Construction of burners   32
            2.4 Transport of the sample into the flame   35
            2.5 Evaporation in the flame   37
            2.6 Reactions in the flame   39
            2.7 Absorption tubes   43
            2.8 Other means for the production of atomic vapours   48

CHAPTER 3   Light sources   51
            3.1 Hollow cathode discharge tubes   51
            3.2 Radiation from hollow cathode lamps   54
            3.3 High brightness hollow cathode lamps   56
            3.4 Operation of hollow cathode lamps   57
            3.5 The manufacture of hollow cathode lamps in the laboratory   58
            3.6 Vapour discharge lamps   60
            3.7 High-frequency electrodeless discharge tubes   62
            3.8 The flame as a source   63
            3.9 Continuous sources   64

CHAPTER 4   Isolation and detection of radiation   65
4.1 General   65
4.2 Monochromators   66
4.3 Light detectors   68

CHAPTER 5   Instrumentation   71
5.1 The direct current measuring device   71
5.2 The modulated measuring system   72
5.3 Double-beam spectrophotometers   73
5.4 Other measuring devices   75
5.5 Review of commercial instruments   77

CHAPTER 6   Sensitivity, precision and accuracy   80
6.1 Sensitivity   80
6.2 Detection limit   81
6.3 Photometric errors   84
6.4 The assessment of specific analytical procedures   86

CHAPTER 7   Experimental Techniques   88
7.1 Instrument operation   88
7.2 Preparation of standard solutions   90
7.3 Evaluation   92
7.4 The choice of the analytical line   95
7.5 Interference effects and their elimination   97
7.6 Unabsorbed parasitic radiation   100
7.7 Background absorption   101

CHAPTER 8   Analytical possibilities of atomic absorption
flame spectrometry   103

CHAPTER 9   Applications   109
9.1 The determination of alkali metals   109
9.1 The determination of alkali earth metals   117
9.3 The determination of non-ferrous metals   127
9.4 The determination of noble metals   138
9.5 The determination of ferrous metals   141
9.6 The determination of gallium, indium and thallium   149
9.7 The determination of arsenic, selenium and tellurium   150
9.8 The determination of refractory elements   151
9.9 Atomic fluorescence spectrometry   155

APPENDIX   Recently published papers   169

References   171
Index   185

FOREWORD

The steadily growing demands on chemical analyses of various materials compel analytical chemists to look for new methods which make the analysis simple, quick and reliable. Therefore spectroscopic methods of analysis possessing all these qualities, have been developed at an increased rate in recent years.

Atomic absorption spectroscopy, sometimes briefly called *atomic absorption*, is one of these latest spectroscopic methods. It is based on the measurement of atomic absorption spectra. Since its origin in 1953, it has been widely used in many analytical laboratories where its speed, sensitivity, precision and specificity* of measurement of many elements are especially valued.

Although the evolution of atomic absorption spectrophotometry is still proceeding at a very high rate we have decided to write this book to propagate the method for use in analytical laboratories. We emphasize the analytical uses of atomic absorption, which take up the greater part of the book. However, for mastering the problems of atomic absorption spectroscopy, knowledge of some basic problems of the absorption of atomic spectra is essential. Therefore, some elementary concepts, such as the oscillator strength of an atom and the absorption coefficient, are also explained, assuming a rough knowledge of college physics by the reader. We simultaneously assume that readers will have some knowledge of the principles and instrumentation of emission flame photometry, which is widely used in many laboratories. If not, several excellent monographs on emission flame photometry are available (3, 7, 9A).

---

* The ability to measure one particular element in presence of many others.

7

The situation in atomic absorption spectrophotometry is less favourable. Only few monographs have so far been published. One by ELWELL and GIDLEY (4) in 1961 with a revised edition in 1966, the second by J. W. ROBINSON (11), the third in Russian by B. V. LVOV (9), the fourth by E. E. ANGINO and G. K. BILLINGS (11 A) and the last by J. RAMÍREZ-MUÑOZ (11 B).* Besides these books, several reviews on atomic absorption spectrophotometry can also be found in different journals.

In our book we have attempted to approach the problems of atomic absorption spectroscopy somewhat differently. We hope we have been at least partly successful and that our book will be helpful to those trying to master this new analytical method.

We are grateful to assistant professor Dr. Bohumil POLEJ of the University of Chemical Technology in Prague and to the late Dr. Josef DVOŘÁK of the Research Institute for Inorganic Chemistry in Ústí for many helpful suggestions and to Dr. Zdeněk ŠULCEK of the Central Geological Institute for his support of our work.

---

* An excellent book recently appeared by Walter LEWIN: *Atomic Absorption Spectroscopy*, Interscience Publications, John Wiley, New York, London, Sydney.

THE HISTORY OF MEASUREMENT OF ATOMIC ABSORPTION SPECTRA

The history of spectroscopy is firmly connected with the observation of atomic absorption spectra in the most common light source, i. e. the sun. As early as in 1802, WOLLASTON observed dark lines in the sun's spectrum. These were then more thoroughly studied by FRAUENHOFER (1814) and bear his name up to today. In 1820, BREWSTER maintained that the FRAUENHOFER lines originated from absorption in the sun's atmosphere, but not before 1859 did KIRCHHOFF and BUNSEN present an exact explanation, which simultaneously laid the foundations of spectrochemical analysis. They proved that the yellow sodium line emitted by a flame into which sodium salts have been introduced, corresponds exactly to the dark D line from the sun's spectrum. The D line might, therefore, be attributed to sodium atoms present in the sun's atmosphere. They also concluded that by observing spectral lines the composition of the atmosphere of the sun and some other stars could be derived.

The relation between emission and absorption spectra was formulated exactly by KIRCHHOFF. According to KIRCHHOFF's law, *all matter absorbs light at the wavelength at which it emits.* This law has a general validity. In practice, however, it is usually applied to gaseous matter.

Later, several research workers tried to determine quantitatively the composition of the sun's atmosphere. To do this the theory of thermal ionization (SAHA 1929) and the theory of line absorption coefficients are essential. An important notion for a quantitative estimation of the concentration of atoms is the so-called "oscillator strength" of the atoms. Experiments based on the measurement of line absorption were carried out in an attempt to measure the oscillator strength of different

139211

elements and different lines. To do this, an exact knowledge of the concentration of free atoms in the absorption medium was essential. The experimental devices, therefore, were relatively complicated. This made their use for chemical analysis unsuitable.

The only exception was the determination of mercury concentration in the air. This element, widely used in industry, is very poisonous and its measurement in the atmosphere presented a serious problem. Due to its particular properties, mercury has sufficiently high vapour pressure even at room temperature, so that the absorption of its resonance line may easily be used for mercury determinations. The first instruments based on this principle were constructed in the early thirties of this century (381).

The use of atomic absorption for other elements was hindered by the difficulties in producing free atoms in a gaseous state. With the development of emission flame photometry it was found that a relatively simple and reproducible method was achieved by the introduction of a finely dispersed sample into a flame. At flame temperatures, most compounds evaporate and dissociate, so that the flame gases contain free atoms of many elements. Despite this well-known fact, the possibility of using such a flame for absorption measurements was left unnoticed.

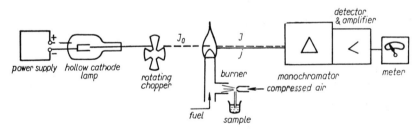

Fig. 1. Schematic diagram of an atomic absorption spectrophotometer
J_0 — *modulated light beam from a hollow cathode lamp, J — the beam after absorption in the flame, j — unmodulated light emitted by the flame*

In 1953 WALSH (350) and, independently but somewhat later, ALKEMADE and MILATZ (14) proposed the use of atomic absorption as a generally applicable analytical method. A simple atomic absorption spectrophotometer was demonstrated in 1954 at the Exhibition of the

Physical Institute in Melbourne. The first analytical applications dealing with agro-chemical analyses were published in 1958 (17, 81).

For a number of elements, however, the temperature of chemical flames is insufficient for the production of free atoms. Therefore, different devices were tried, among which was a modification of the KING's furnace (211) previously used for the measurement of oscillator

Fig. 2. Commercial atomic absorption spectrophotometer AA4 (by courtesy of Techtron Pty, Melbourne)

strengths. However, all these methods for the production of atomic vapour are much more complicated than a flame and are, therefore, only seldom used. Atomic absorption spectrophotometry using the flame as the absorbing medium is sometimes called absorption flame photometry.

To conclude this chapter, let us briefly describe an *instrument for atomic absorption spectrophotometry*, the basic scheme of which is reproduced in Fig. 1. The radiation from the light source passes through the absorption medium. The dispersion unit isolates the measured resonance line from the other lines emitted by the light source and the resulting radiation flux is measured by the detection system. Hollow cathode lamps are usually used as light sources because the emitted spectrum has many desirable properties, i.e. low background and narrow lines (by low background, low light intensity at wavelengths other than in the region of the spectral line being measured, is meant). A picture of an atomic absorption spectrophotometer, the Techtron model AA4, is reproduced as an example (see Fig. 2).

CHAPTER 1

THE ABSORPTION OF RADIATION BY FREE ATOMS

1.1 OSCILLATOR STRENGTH

Atomic absorption spectroscopy is based on the measurement of the *absorption of resonance radiation by free atoms in the gaseous state*, i.e. of spectral lines corresponding to the transition of atoms between the ground and excited states. For the quantitative treatment of this process some basic relations will be given. To this end we shall need the term density of radiation ϱ, which is the amount of radiative energy in unit volume of a sample. If the amount of radiative energy in a unit frequency interval only is considered, we speak of the so-called spectral density of radiation, denoted by ϱ_v. Let us assume that in a small frequency interval $(v,\ v + \Delta v)$ the spectral density ϱ_v is constant and that the resonance line frequency v_{ik} lies in this interval (in the following

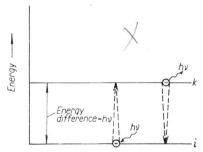

Fig. 1.1. Transition between two energy levels i and k. The transition is accompanied by emission or absorption of a light quantum

text the *ik* index of the frequency symbol will be omitted). If free atoms are in such an electromagnetic field, radiative energy (light quanta) is absorbed, causing the transition of some atoms from the ground to the excited state (Fig. 1.1). The *total energy absorbed per second in a unit volume* is evidently proportional to the number n of free atoms in the ground state, to the radiation density ϱ_v, to the energy $h\nu$ of the light photons absorbed and to the probability of absorption B_{ik}. Therefore

$$E_{abs} = nB_{ik}\varrho_v h\nu \tag{1.1}$$

holds. B_{ik}, the proportionality constant, is the EINSTEIN probability coefficient for absorption. The index ik indicates that due to absorption a transition of the atom from the ground state i to the excited state k takes place. These transition probabilities differ for individual lines and are connected with the electronic configurations of the two states. The probability coefficient B_{ik} is not a dimensionless number as is usual in the probability calculus. The product $B_{ik}\varrho_v$ expresses the ratio of atoms which absorb a photon with the energy $h\nu_{ik}$ per unit time to the total number of atoms present in the ground state. The dimension of this product is, therefore, $[\sec^{-1}]$.

The atom may also be considered as a forced *electric dipole oscillator* formed by two point charges of equal magnitude but of opposite sign. The positive charge has a fixed position whereas the negative charge can oscillate around it. This negative charge is made up of all the atomic electrons, all or only some of which may be set into forced notion by the field. According to electrodynamic laws the total energy absorbed by this classical harmonic oscillator in unit time may be expressed as

$$E_{abs} = f\frac{\pi e^2}{m}\varrho_v, \tag{1.2}$$

where e is the electronic charge, m the electron mass, and f a dimensionless factor, the so-called absorption oscillator strength. (Thus, f represents the effective number of classical free electron oscillators which, by their absorption effect, are equal to the absorption effect of the atom for the given transition.*) Equating the energies in eqs. (1.1) and (1.2) the following expression for this *absorption oscillator strength* may be derived

$$f_{ik} = \frac{mh\nu}{\pi e^2}B_{ik}. \tag{1.3}$$

---

* See for example, KUHN: *Atomic Spectra*, Longmans Green, 64.

Oscillator strengths for the main lines of most elements are listed in Table 9.13 at the end of the book. When dealing with emission to the ground state, the *emission oscillator strength* f_{ki} is sometimes used. The mutual relation is

$$g_i f_{ki} = -g_k f_{ik}$$

where g_k and g_i are the statistical weights of the excited and ground state respectively (i.e. the g factors represent the number of atomic levels, both ZEEMAN and hyperfine which constitute the actual state).

1.2 ATOMIC ABSORPTION COEFFICIENT

For atomic absorption the *atomic absorption coefficient* is an important quantity. It may be derived from the following notion: A parallel light beam with radiation density ϱ_v is falling on a layer of unit area and of thickness dl (see Fig. 1.2). For the sake of simplicity a parallel beam is assumed. The probability coefficient B_{ik} used here is, therefore, somewhat different

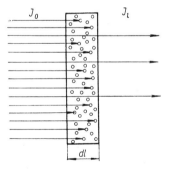

Fig. 1.2. Absorption of radiation in a thin isotropic layer J_0 — radiation flux density of the incident radiation, J_l — radiation flux density after passing the layer of thickness dl

from EINSTEIN's original definition, because he assumed isotropic radiation. The total number of ground state atoms in the considered volume element is $n \cdot dl$, where n is the number of atoms in unit volume. According to eq. (1.1) the total energy absorbed in the given volume per unit time is

$$E_{abs} = B_{ik} h \nu \varrho_v n \, dl \, . \tag{1.4}$$

In that same time, radiation energy $c\varrho_v$ passes through this layer (where c is the velocity of light). This represents the number $c\varrho_v/hv$ of photons. If the effective cross section for one atom for the absorption of a light quantum is defined as $\varkappa_{ik}$ then in the considered unit area the total absorbing area will be $\varkappa_{ik}n\,dl$. The number of photons of energy h absorbed may be expressed as $\varkappa_{ik}n\,dlc\varrho_v/hv$. The total energy absorbed is given by the product of the number of photons and their energy, i.e.

$$E_{\text{abs}} = \varkappa_{ik}n\,dlc\varrho_v . \tag{1.5}$$

From eqs. (1.4) and (1.5) the effective atomic cross section (which is nothing else but the atomic absorption coefficient) may be found

$$\varkappa_{ik} = \frac{hv}{c}\,B_{ik} \tag{1.6a}$$

or by using eq. (1.3)

$$\varkappa_{ik} = \frac{\pi e^2}{mc}\,f_{ik} . \tag{1.6b}$$

Equations (1.6a, 1.6b) although derived for parallel radiation generally also hold for non-parallel radiation, because the appropriate geometric factors which we have to introduce for the purpose of correcting the absorbed energy in eqs. (1.4) and (1.5) would in both cases be identical and would cancel out.

The dimension of the atomic absorption coefficient is [length^2] as may be expected for a cross section. An absorption coefficient K related to unit volume is often used. Its dimension is [length^{-1}] and both coefficients are related by the equation

$$K = n\varkappa ,$$

where n is again the number of atoms in unit volume.

In this derivation of the atomic absorption coefficient, the equilibrium between excited and ground state atoms, has been neglected. That is we have omitted the number of atoms not available for absorption, because they are already excited. Besides spontaneous emission, excited atoms in an electromagnetic field also undergo stimulated emission at a rate proportional to strength of the field. This stimulated emission, also referred to as negative absorption, brings about a reduction in the absorption coefficient. This is because the stimulated emission process adds a photon to the field of the incident beam and hence compensates in part for the absorption. Taking this phenomenon into account the expression for the absorption coefficient is:

$$\varkappa_{ik} = \frac{h\nu}{c} \left(1 - \frac{n_k g_i}{n_i g_k} \right) B_{ik} ,$$

where n with the appropriate index indicates the number of ground state or excited atoms in a volume unit and g_k, g_i are the statistical weights of the two states respectively (see p. 15). However, since the ratio n_k/n_i is under usual conditions small, the second term in the parentheses on the right side of the equation is negligible compared with unity, may be omitted and eq. (1.6a) again results.

1.3 LINE PROFILES

The absorption coefficient expressed in eqs. (1.6a, b) applies to the spectral line resulting from an atomic transition between the i and k energy levels. However, the line is not infinitely narrow but covers a definite although relatively narrow frequency interval.* If we relate the absorption coefficient to unit frequency interval and plot this so-called spectral absorption coefficient $\varkappa_\nu$ against frequency, the *absorption line profile* results (Fig. 1.3). The atomic absorption coefficient given by eq. (1.6) refers to the total number of photons absorbed of all energies present in the spectral line and is an integral coefficient given by

$$\varkappa_{ik} = \varkappa_{L} = \int_0^\infty \varkappa_\nu \, d\nu . \tag{1.7}$$

The index L indicates that an integral quantity is involved, concerning the whole line. The integration boundaries should only strictly cover the frequency interval of the line profile. When extending the interval from zero to infinity we disregard the presence of other spectral lines.

---

* This is the "natural width" of the radiation — see KUHN: *Atomic Spectra*, Longmans Green, 382 (1969).

Inasmuch as most spectral lines are symmetrical, it is convenient for simplicity's sake to introduce the variable $u = v_{ik} - v$. The integration boundaries then extend from $-\infty$ to $+\infty$. The line profile may further be expressed as the product of the integral absorption coefficient and the so-called *profile function* $P(u)$ which is defined so that the relations

$$\int_{-\infty}^{+\infty} P(u)\, du = 1 \qquad (1.8)$$

and

$$\varkappa(u) = \varkappa_{\mathrm{L}} P(u) \qquad (1.9)$$

hold, with $P(u)$ centred at $u = 0$.

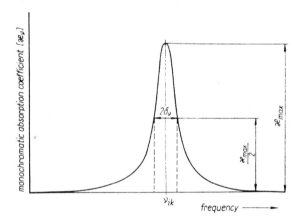

Fig. 1.3. Profile of an absorption line (i. e. the *frequency dependence of the mono-chromatic absorption coefficient*)
$2\delta v$ — the line width

An important characteristic of the line profile is the so-called *line-width*, which is defined as the frequency (wave number or wavelength) difference on the line profile of the two points corresponding to half the maximum value of the absorption coefficient $\varkappa(v)$ (see Fig. 1.3). This value is sometimes referred to as the half-width. We prefer to call the half-width half of this value marked δ on Fig. 1.3.

The spectral line width is influenced by several factors. For practical conditions in gases, apart from the natural line-width due to the finite lifetime of the atom itself in the excited state, only two factors have to be taken into account. As a result of the disordered thermal motion of atoms, the radiation emitted or absorbed is subject to the DOPPLER effect. The profile function is, therefore, due in this case to a Maxwellian distribution of atomic velocities and may be expressed as a Gaussian function

$$P(u) = \sqrt{\left(\frac{\ln 2}{\pi}\right)} \frac{1}{\delta} \exp\left[-\left(\frac{u}{\delta}\right)^2 \ln 2\right]. \tag{1.10}$$

For the DOPPLER *line-width* the following relation holds

$$\delta = \frac{v}{c} \sqrt{\frac{2RT \ln 2}{M}} = 3.59v \sqrt{\frac{T}{M}}, \tag{1.11}$$

where T is absolute temperature and M the atomic weight (see ref. 10). The DOPPLER line width is, therefore, greater in the case of elements of low atomic weight and becomes larger with increasing temperature.

The second factor to be considered is impact or *pressure broadening*. The frequency of a spectral line is given by the difference of the two atom energy levels involved in the transition. However, the energy of both levels is slightly influenced by the atom interacting with the surrounding particles and this brings about a variation in the frequency of the light quanta emitted or absorbed, whereby a broadening of the spectral line results.* According to the nature of the interaction several broadening effects may be discerned. If electrically charged particles are involved, we speak of STARK broadening; in the case of interaction with dissimilar non-charged particles the effect is called VAN DER WAALS broadening and for interactions with atoms of the same kind as the radiating atoms it is called resonance broadening. All three effects are often referred to as impact or LORENTZ broadening. In all three cases the resulting profile function may be expressed by the so-called resonance function (i.e. it has a Lorentzian shape)

$$P(u) = \frac{1}{\pi} \frac{1}{u^2 + \delta^2}, \tag{1.12}$$

---

* See, for example, KUHN: *Atomic Spectra*, Longmans Green, 395.

where the half-width δ is proportional to the concentration of the inter-acting particles. The resonance profile falls off much less steeply $(\sim u^{-2})$ than the Gaussian profile $(\sim \exp[-u^2])$.

However, in a number of cases both profiles, i.e. the resonance and the Gaussian profile, take place simultaneously and from their mutual combination results the so-called Voigt profile which is given by a more complicated function

$$P(u) = \frac{1}{\delta} \sqrt{\left(\frac{\ln 2}{\pi}\right)} \frac{a}{\pi} \int_{-\infty}^{+\infty} \frac{e^{-y}\,dy}{a^2 + (v-y)^2} ,$$

where $a = \delta_{\text{impact}} \sqrt{\ln 2}/\delta_{\text{Doppler}}$ is substantially the ratio of the half-widths corresponding to the impact and Doppler broadening, $v = u/\delta_{\text{Doppler}}\sqrt{\ln 2}$ and y is the integration variable. Values of the Voigt profile may be found in several tables (5, 270).*

The contributions of DOPPLER and impact broadening to the resultant line naturally depends on the element involved, on the properties of the particular line measured and on experimental conditions. Table 1.1 gives values found experimentally for some elements and lines in an

Table 1.1

HALF-WIDTHS OF SEVERAL LINES IN AN ACETYLENE-AIR FLAME
ACCORDING TO N. N. SOBOLEV, SPECTROCHIM. ACTA **11**, 310 (1956)

Line † nm	Total half-width	Doppler half-width	Collision half-width
Na 589·0	0·009	0·003	0·006
Li 670·8	0·013	0·006	0·007
Ca 422·7	0·006	0·002	0·004
Tl 535·0	0·006	0·001	0·005

acetylene-air flame. Calculated values for different flames and most elements are listed in (260).

---

* See also H. C. VAN DE HULST: *Astophys. J.* **106**, 121 (1947) 83.

C. W. ALLEN: *Astrophysical Quantities*, Athlone Press, 83 (1955).

† See footnote, p. 27.

1.4 THE BEER-LAMBERT LAW

So far only absorption of radiation in a unit volume has been considered. In practice the quantity called *radiation flux density J* is measured, i.e. the energy passing through a unit area perpendicular to the light beam in unit time. For a parallel beam a simple relation exists between the radiation density and the radiation flux

$$J = \varrho c . \qquad (1.13)$$

Let dJ_v be an infinitesimal increase in the spectral radiation flux density J_v. Then assuming monochromatic radiation and rewriting eq. (1.5) for a *spectral absorption coefficient*, the absorbed energy in the volume element considered equals the decrease of the incident radiation flux density $-dJ_v$

$$-dJ_v = \varkappa_v n \, dlJ_v$$

or

$$dJ_v/J_v = -\varkappa_v n \, dl . \qquad (1.14)$$

For a homogeneous layer, i.e. if $\varkappa_v$ and n are independent of the distance l, this equation may be integrated along the path length l. Inserting the boundary conditions, that is for $l = 0$, $J_{v,l} = J_{v,0}$, the BEER-LAMBERT Law results:

$$J_{v,l} = J_{v,0} \exp\left(-\varkappa_v n l\right) . \qquad (1.15)$$

Here, $J_{v,0}$ and $J_{v,l}$ are the radiation flux densities before and after passing through a uniform layer of thickness l. Putting eq. (1.15) into logarithmic form, the important relation between the natural logarithm of their ratio and *concentration of* atoms results

$$\ln\left(J_{v,0}/J_{v,l}\right) = \varkappa_v n l . \qquad (1.16)$$

Because it is more convenient to work with logarithms to base ten this equation is usually transformed to

$$A = \log\left(J_{v,0}/J_{v,l}\right) = 2.303 \, \varkappa_v n l ,$$

where A is defined as the *absorbance*.

In practice, it is not monochromatic radiation which is measured but all the radiation in a definite frequency interval (the so-called spectral band-width) isolated by the application of a monochromator or filter. Let us now consider how this fact influences the absorbance values measured. For line spectra, both $\varkappa_v$ and J_v vary considerably in the measured spectral pass band. Using profile functions the frequency dependence of the radiation flux density may be expressed by analogy with eq. (1.8) as

$$J_0(u) = J_{L,0}P'(u) \quad \text{and} \quad J_l(u) = J_{L,l}P''(u) \tag{1.17}$$

(the shape of the lines may be different before and after the absorption). Quantities relating to the emission profile, as distinguished from the absorption profile, are designated by symbols marked with primes. Inserting eqs. (1.9) and (1.17) into (1.15) we obtain

$$J_{L,l}P''(u) = J_{L,0}P'(u) \exp\left[-\varkappa_L P(u)\,nl\right] \tag{1.18}$$

and after integration in the whole frequency interval

$$J_{L,l} = J_{L,0} \int_{-\infty}^{+\infty} P'(u) \exp\left[-\varkappa_L P(u)\,nl\right] \mathrm{d}u \,. \tag{1.19}$$

This equation expresses the BEER-LAMBERT Law for non-monochromatic radiation when spectral distributions must be considered. The result evidently depends on the profile functions of both lines, i.e. of the emission as well as absorption line (383). When using sources radiating lines, the profile function $P'(u)$ is given by the emission line profile. If light sources with continuous spectra are used, the emission profile is controlled by the slit function of the monochromator and depends on the width of the entrance and exit slits.

1.5 THE RELATION BETWEEN ABSORBANCE AND CONCENTRATION OF ATOMS

From eq. (1.19) the relation between absorbance and atomic concentration may be derived. However, from the form of the equation it will be seen that the influence of both emission and absorption profile functions on this relation is complicated. Therefore, let us introduce an *effective absorption coefficient*, which we define as a fictitious quantity resulting from the measurement if we were to apply the BEER-LAMBERT Law for monochromatic radiation to our non-monochromatic system. By comparison of eqs. (1.19) and (1.15), we find the following relation for this effective absorption coefficient.

$$\exp\left[-\varkappa_{\text{eff}} nl\right] = \int_{-\infty}^{+\infty} P'(u) \exp\left[-\varkappa_{\text{L}} P(u)\, nl\right] du.$$

If both the exponential terms are expanded into series, we have

$$\varkappa_{\text{eff}} nl - \frac{(\varkappa_{\text{eff}} nl)^2}{2!} + \dots =$$

$$\varkappa_{\text{L}} nl \int_{-\infty}^{+\infty} P(u)\, P'(u)\, du - \frac{(\varkappa_{\text{L}} nl)^2}{2!} \int_{-\infty}^{+\infty} P^2(u)\, P'(u)\, du + \dots. \quad (1.20)$$

From this equation it may be seen that the effective absorption coefficient depends not only on both profile functions but also on the product $\varkappa_{\text{L}} nl$ i.e. also on the so-called *optical depth*. For very small values of this optical depth we need only take into account the terms involving the first power of the depth on the right and left side of eq. (1.20) and a limiting value for the effective absorption coefficient may be derived.

$$\varkappa_{\text{eff.lim}} = \varkappa_{\text{L}} \int_{-\infty}^{+\infty} P'(u)\, P(u)\, du. \quad (1.21)$$

Geometrically $\varkappa_{\text{eff.lim}}$ defines the slope at zero concentration in the relation between absorbance and concentration of free atoms.

If both emission and absorption lines have resonance profiles, the following relation for this limiting value of the absorption coefficient is obtained by integration of eq. (1.21)

$$\varkappa_{\text{eff.lim}} = \frac{\varkappa_{\text{L}}}{\pi(\delta + \delta')}. \quad (1.22\text{a})$$

For DOPPLER shaped lines the analogous expression would be

$$\varkappa_{\text{eff.lim}} = \frac{\varkappa_{\text{L}} \sqrt{\ln 2}}{\sqrt{\pi(\delta^2 + \delta'^2)}}. \quad (1.22\text{b})$$

From eqs. (1.22a, b) it follows that the slope at the zero concentration
point, and hence the correlated sensitivity of measurement, are proportional to the reciprocal value of the sum of both line half-widths
for resonance profiles or to the square root of the sum of squares
for DOPPLER shaped lines, irrespective of whether the absorption or
the emission line is broader. However, the further course of this
dependence differs according to which of the two lines is broader. The
resulting *bending* may be evaluated by solving eq. (1.19). This and similar
equations were solved numerically for different line shapes and different
line-width ratios. The results have been tabulated (10), or expressed
graphically (271).

It has been found that bending starts at lower absorbance values and
is more pronounced with increasing emission to absorption line-width
ratio. For a given ratio, resonance shaped lines manifest a more pronounced bending than DOPPLER shaped lines. In atomic absorption
spectroscopy hollow cathode lamps are usually used as light sources
and it is often true that the emission line-width due to these is much
smaller than the absorption line-width in flames. In this case, the effective
absorption coefficient value can be approximated to the maximum
value of the monochromatic one and a simple relation results for resonance profiles,

$$A = 2 \cdot 303 \varkappa_{max} nl = \frac{\varkappa_L}{\pi \delta} nl .$$ (1.23a)

Similarly for Gaussian profiles,

$$A = 2 \cdot 303 \frac{\varkappa_L \, nl}{\delta} \sqrt{\frac{\ln 2}{\pi}} .$$ (1.23b)

However, this assumption is not quite correct in all instances. Spectral
line-widths emitted from currently used hollow cathode lamps with
non-cooled cathodes measure about $0.01 - 0.04$ Å. The line profiles are
moreover often distorted by self-absorption in the hollow cathode
itself and this considerably increases the apparent line-width. If, for
example, the emission line-width is half the absorption line-width, the
resulting absorbance will be about 10% lower at the absorbance value

$A = 1$ than the straight line value. Increasing the absorption line-width by, for example, increased pressure in the absorption medium often causes straightening analytical curves (213).

Several other effects can be used to explain the bending of analytical curves. If the line-width were fully-controlled by resonance broadening, which is proportional to the concentration of the particular element, no absorbance increase with element concentration would be observed. However, this effect should be evident only for very high concentrations which are not realized in analytical work (288).

Another possible reason for analytical curve bending is the hyperfine structure of spectral lines caused by isotope shift and nuclear spin. As a result of these factors, most spectral lines are composed of several components with wavelength differences so small that due to the previous mentioned broadening effects, they usually appear as a single line. Only for very light or very heavy elements, does the wavelength difference of the individual components exceed the line-width. The bending of the absorbance − concentration curve is in these cases given by the number, wavelength difference and intensity of the individual hyperfine structure components (213, 379).

In general, one can say that bending always takes place when the radiation in the spectral interval of the emission line is not absorbed uniformly, i.e. when the absorption coefficient $\varkappa_\nu$ is not constant within this spectral interval.

In practical analysis the bending of analytical curves is frequently caused by the presence, in the radiation flux measured, of some radiation not subject to absorption (235). This non-absorbed radiation may in the first place be stray light with a wavelength quite different from the wavelength measured, or it may appertain to some spectral line emitted by the light source in the spectral band-width measured. For example, a spectral emission line of a rare gas from the hollow cathode tube filling (313) or of some foreign element present in the hollow cathode or supporting material may give rise to bending. It may even be a non-resonant line of the element being determined. This happens very often when elements rich in emission line spectra (e.g. iron, cobalt, nickel) are involved. It may also be a continuous "background" radiation very often due to the presence of hydrogen. In all these cases the absorbance measured may be expressed as

$$A = \log \frac{J_{L,0} + J'}{J_{L,l} + J'},$$ (1.24)

where J' is the radiation flux density not subject to absorption. With increasing absorption of the resonance line this absorbance does not become infinite but tends towards a limiting value of

$$A = \log \frac{J_{L,0} + J'}{J'}$$ (1.25)

which cannot be exceeded, and as a result the analytical curves manifest a more or less severe bending, depending on the relative values of $J_{L,0}$ and J' (271).

1.6. THERMAL EXCITATION

Free atoms in the absorption medium may also undergo thermal excitation. The fraction of excited atoms may be expressed by the well-known BOLTZMANN equation

$$n_k/n_i = (g_k/g_i) \exp [-E_k/kT]$$ (1.26)

where E_k is the excitation energy, g_k and g_i the statistical weights of the excited and ground states respectively (see p. 15). Inserting the value of the BOLTZMANN constant k in eV/°C and transforming the natural logarithm to base ten, a suitable form for numerical calculations results

$$n_k/n_i = (g_k/g_i) \, 10^{-5'040E_k/T},$$ (1.27)

where T is the absolute temperature.

Because the wavelength of the resonance lines is inversely proportional to their energy $E_k = hv = hc/\lambda$, where c is the velocity of light, the portion of excited atoms grows exponentially with increasing resonance line wavelength. In an acetylene-air flame with a temperature of approximately 2.500°K about 0.17% of potassium atoms are in the excited state corresponding to the line at 776 nm.* For strontium at 461 nm the appropriate number is $1 . 10^{-3}\%$, for magnesium at 285 nm $6 . 10^{-7}\%$ and for zinc at 214 nm $6 . 10^{-10}\%$. All these numbers are negligible compared with the number of atoms in the ground state. However, the radiation emitted by these atoms when returning to the ground state might not be negligible. The resulting radiation density is given by the equation

$$\varrho_{ik} = A_{ki} n_k h\nu_{ik} \qquad (1.28)$$

where A_{ki} is the EINSTEIN probability coefficient of spontaneous emission. Thus, this radiation entering the optical system and falling on the detector, influences the measured absorption. In the ultraviolet region below 300 nm, the radiation from an acetylene-air flame is negligible. However, for longer wavelengths the flame emission must be added to the radiation from the light source, causing bending of the graph of concentration against absorbance (301). In hotter flames radiation of even shorter wavelength must be expected.

To eliminate this influence, the radiation from the light source is modulated and only the synchronously alternating part of the photo-current is amplified and measured. Radiation from the flame which is not modulated does not assert itself. The perfectness of elimination depends on the frequency band-width used and on the stability of the flame emission. These questions will be dealt with in greater detail in Chapter 5.

1.7 ATOMIC RESONANCE FLUORESCENCE

Free atoms in the absorbing medium are also excited by absorption of a light quantum. Although usually in the flame a much greater part of the excited atoms return to the ground state by collisions of the second kind without emitting radiation, a small proportion rapidly re-emit the light quanta absorbed. This process is called atomic resonance fluorescence.

---

* In this book, the nanometre (nm) is a frequently used unit of wavelength, instead of the more commonly used ANGSTRÖM unit. The relation between them is $1 \text{ nm} = 10 \text{ Å}$.

Fluorescent radiation is naturally modulated with the same frequency as the exciting radiation from the light source and is, therefore, also registered by the measuring device. Under conditions used in atomic absorption, resonance fluorescence is negligible. However, if the experimental arrangement is changed and the modulated radiation perpendicular to the exciting beam is observed (16, 375) only atomic fluorescence may be measured. The method of atomic absorption fluorescence is based on this principle.

Disregarding re-absorption of fluorescent radiation, a simple relationship between the concentration of the element and its fluorescent radiation may be derived. For more detailed discussion, including reabsorption, see 375.

Fluorescent radiation energy emitted J_F is proportional to the total radiation energy absorbed J_{abs}

$$J_F = \Phi J_{abs} \qquad (1.29)$$

where Φ is the quantum efficiency of the fluorescent process, i.e. it is the ratio of atoms leaving a particular excited state by emission of fluorescent radiation to all atoms leaving this state in unit time. Using the expression for the absorbed energy from the BEER-LAMBERT Law, we get

$$J_F = \Phi J_0 [1 - \exp(-\varkappa nl)] . \qquad (1.30)$$

For low concentrations of free atoms (n), the exponential term may be expanded in a series and the third and higher terms neglected. Expression (1.30) is thus simplified to

$$J_F = \Phi J_0 \varkappa nl . \qquad (1.31)$$

From this equation the influence of several factors is evident. The sensitivity of determination depends on the atomic absorption coefficient $\varkappa$, on the absorption path length l, on the quantum efficiency Φ and on the flux density of the incident radiation J_0. It may, therefore, be expected that improvement of the light sources used will bring a corresponding improvement in the sensitivity of determination.

CHAPTER 2

ABSORPTION MEDIA

In the preceding chapter we have discussed how light absorption is related to the concentration of free atoms in the absorbing medium. In this chapter we shall deal with the different means of producing such a cloud of free atoms which, with the exception of inert gases, is not stable under normal conditions.

The different methods of preparing absorbing media should fulfil several requirements. The concentration of free atoms in the absorbing medium should be as high as possible and the proportionality between it and the concentration in the sample solution should not vary. For analytical use it is also important that the technique should be simple and reproducible. All the methods used up till now are not without drawbacks. It is generally expected that further development in atomic absorption greatly depends on the improvement of methods for producing atomic vapours.

So far the use of chemical flames has enjoyed the greatest popularity. This is partly due to the fact that this technique was taken over from emission flame photometry which was already well developed, and partly due to its simplicity and the ease with which it can be applied. One of its major disadvantages, the relatively low temperature insufficient for atomization of some elements, has been recently overcome by introducing new gas mixtures, (e. g. a nitrous oxide — acetylene mixture), giving flames with considerably higher temperatures. This fact will probably keep the privileged position of chemical flames in atomic absorption unchallenged for the next couple of years.

2.1 THE FLAME

The flame is a well-known phenomenon of everyday life. It originates by chemical reaction between a fuel and an oxidant. In flame photometry both the fuel and the oxidant are gaseous, the oxidant being usually air or oxygen. To ensure a steady state reaction, the combustion process is controlled in a special device, *the burner.*

Disregarding the different possible gas mixtures two groups of flames can be distinguished. The flames of the first group are the so called *premixed flames* which originate by combustion of a fuel and oxidant mixture. The resulting flame exhibits a laminar flow and is, therefore, sometimes called the *laminar flame.* Its most remarkable feature is a well-defined reaction zone. For hydrocarbon fuels this reaction zone (sometimes called the inner zone) is clearly discernible by its blue-green light. With a little practice the flow ratio of the fuel and oxidant may be estimated from the size and colour of the zone.

For the second group of flames the fuel and oxidant are first mixed in the flame itself. By combustion a *strong turbulence* results and the reaction zone is, therefore, not so well defined.

Both types of flames have their advantages and drawbacks. For atomic absorption laminar premixed flames are more often used.

2.2 FLAME MIXTURES USED IN ABSORPTION FLAME PHOTOMETRY

In atomic absorption only some of the many mixtures so far tried in emission flame photometry have been applied. For laminar premixed flames it is difficult to use oxygen as oxidant, because the burning velocity of the resulting gas mixtures is too high and a flashback is likely to occur. For a steady flame the streaming velocity of the gas mixture through the burner head must be greater than the burning velocity. With oxygen this would require a relatively high pressure in the cloud chamber and a small total area for the opening in the burner head, i.e. very narrow holes or a very narrow slot (218). This would easily become clogged by crystallization of salts or condensation of soot.

For these reasons air is usually used, although its nitrogen content reduces the resulting temperature considerably. In Table 2.1 important data on some of the more often used mixtures is given. As already mentioned, the *burning velocity* determines the minimum streaming velocity,

Table 2.1

PROPERTIES OF SOME FUEL-OXIDANT MIXTURES

Fuel oxidant mixture	Ignition temperature °C	Burning velocity cm/sec	Flame temperature °C
coal gas-air	560	55	1,840
coal gas-oxygen	450		2,730
propane⎫ butane⎭-air	510	82·1	1,935
propane⎫ butane⎭-oxygen	490		2,850
hydrogen-air	530	440	2,045
hydrogen-oxygen	450	3,680	2,660
acetylene-air	350	160	2,125
acetylene-oxygen	335	2,480	3,100
acetylene-nitrous oxide	400	180	2,955
acetylene-nitric oxide		90	3,080
cyanogen-air		20	2,330
cyanogen-oxygen		140	4,467

the *temperature of ignition* determines the temperature the burner head should not exceed, and the *flame temperature* characterizes the possibilities of the flame for evaporating and dissociating different compounds.

From this point of view flames with a higher temperature should generally be preferred, because they ensure complete evaporation of even the less volatile compounds. This, however, in not always true, as a temperature rise may also have some unfavourable effects. The flame emission increases, the absorption lines are broadened due to the DOPPLER effect and the number of atoms in a unit volume decreases, according to the universal gas laws, so that a sensitivity decrease results.

Moreover the degree of ionization of elements with low ionization eneries increasse so that different interfering effects may take place. The use of high temperature flames is, therefore, not advantageous in all cases.

In the early years of atomic absorption spectroscopy low temperature flames (coal gas-air, propane-air) were usually used. These are suitable for volatile and easily dissociated elements, such as copper, silver, gold, zinc, cadmium, mercury and the alkali metals. However, for a number of elements the temperature of these flames is insufficient. In these cases, hydrogen-air or acetylene-air should be used. For elements forming refractory compounds still higher temperatures are required. Here, an *acetylene-nitrous oxide* (27, 367) or an acetylene-nitric oxide flame (221) is recommended.

The higher temperature of these flames is partly due to the lower nitrogen content and partly to the exothermic decomposition of nitrous oxide. Although the oxygen content is higher, the burning velocity is limited by this decomposition reaction, so that work with a mixture of acetylene and nitrous oxide is quite safe. A corresponding mixture of oxygen has a much higher burning velocity and the danger of a flash-back is considerably greater.

With the nitrous oxide-acetylene flame the concentration measurement of Be, Al, Si, Ti, Zr, V, Sc, the rare earths, etc., is possible. The sensitivities attained for a typical commercial instrument are given in Table 8.1. Because in this flame many of the elements are ionized, the addition of some alkali metal salt is recommended to attain the highest sensitivity (see later).

2.3 CONSTRUCTION OF BURNERS

The burner construction for the two different types of flame is naturally quite different (see Fig. 2.1). For the *total consumption burners* the atomizer's spray is placed directly in the burner whereas for *laminar flow burners* the sprayer (atomizer*) is placed in a *cloud chamber* where mixing

---

* The word atomizer is convenient though somewhat misleading — no atoms are formed but a fine aerosol of droplets are produced from the solution. The word nebulizer is more exact but less commonly used.

of the fuel and oxidant also takes place. The burning of pre-mixed fuel and oxidant poses certain restrictions on the burner parameters if flash-back is not to occur. In a total consumption burner with external

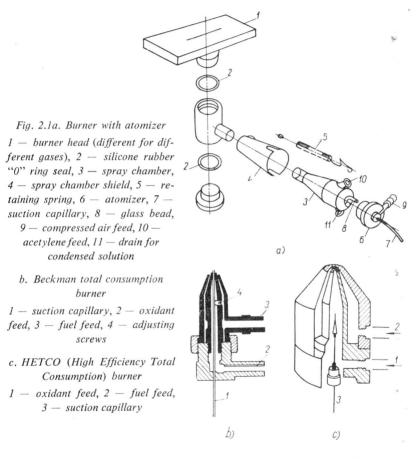

Fig. 2.1a. Burner with atomizer

1 — burner head (different for different gases), 2 — silicone rubber "0" ring seal, 3 — spray chamber, 4 — spray chamber shield, 5 — retaining spring, 6 — atomizer, 7 — suction capillary, 8 — glass bead, 9 — compressed air feed, 10 — acetylene feed, 11 — drain for condensed solution

b. Beckman total consumption burner

1 — suction capillary, 2 — oxidant feed, 3 — fuel feed, 4 — adjusting screws

c. HETCO (High Efficiency Total Consumption) burner

1 — oxidant feed, 2 — fuel feed, 3 — suction capillary

mixture any combination of fuel and oxidant is admissible without any danger. The only requirement is that the flow of the oxidant and fuel be in the appropriate ratio. The gases which may be used with the particular burners are always given by the producer.

As mentioned above, the sensitivity depends on the absorption path length and, therefore, laminar flow burners up to 15 cm long have been constructed. The gas flow needed for such a long burner is naturally higher than for normal burners used in emission flame photometry. From simple reasoning it is evident that the sensitivity with such a burner will increase only so far as the solution sprayed per unit time may be correspondingly increased. Otherwise the sample will only be more diluted by the flame gases and the sensitivity will remain unchanged (194).

Laminar flow burners may be constructed as slot burners, or as MÉKER type burners, which have separate circular holes arranged in one or more rows. The former are gaining popularity, because their construction is simpler and may easily be cleaned if clogged. Construction of slot burners for coal gas, propane, hydrogen and acetylene has been described in detail (74, 124). Their main disadvantage is that the resulting flame is very narrow, so that part of the radiation may pass around the flame. This part is then not absorbed, the sensitivity of determination is decreased and a bending of the working curves takes place. To avoid this, slot burners with many slots perpendicular to the optical axis (389) or with three slots parallel to the optical axis (51) have been constructed.

Burners are usually constructed from large blocks of stainless steel or cast iron to withstand deformation at a high temperature. For highly corrosive acid solutions, plastic burners (61) or glass burners (298) have been used. The burner heads may be made from gilded brass, tantalum sheet or some other non-corrosive material. They must be water-cooled.

Some workers recommend cooling the burner heads, claiming that a stable flame temperature is attained sooner, so that slow drifts in the absorbance values measured are eliminated (208). However, when using acetylene, an excessive cooling may bring about condensation of soot and consequent clogging of the burner slot. This obviously has a negative influence of the stability of measurement.

The nitrous oxide-acetylene flame requires a special burner capable of withstanding temperatures up to several hundred degrees Centigrade (27, 221), and of dissipating the heat generated. Burning acetylene with a mixture of oxygen and nitrogen requires special burners with very narrow slots and a high excess pressure in the cloud chamber (some $15-20$ cm of water), to ensure a high streaming velocity. Mixtures of up to 85% oxygen were tried. Work with these flames is not pleasant, because the danger of flash-back imposes strict rules on handling. The acetylene must be turned on first and the oxygen-nitrogen mixtures added after the flame is lit. (27). In turning off the flame, the process is reversed. Another approach consists in lighting an acetylene-air flame first. The air is then gradually enriched with oxygen (218).

These difficulties may be avoided if a direct sprayer burner for acetylene-oxygen is used. However, when burning fuel-rich mixtures the resulting flame has a high background noise. The situation may be improved by placing a graphite premixing channel below the burner tip. This ensures the premixing of the two gases (188) so that the resulting flame approaches a laminar one and is steady even for fuel-rich mixtures.

2.4 TRANSPORT OF THE SAMPLE INTO THE FLAME

To ensure the instantaneous evaporation of the sample, it must be introduced into the flame in a finely dispersed state. To this end, *pneumatic atomizers**) producing a mist of the sample solution are usually used. Ultrasonic or electrostatic atomizers (97) have also been tried, but their improved performance does not compensate for the complications involved.

The mist from pneumatic atomizers may be either admitted directly into the flame, as with the total consumption burners, or it may beforehand pass through a *cloud chamber* where the bigger droplets are separated by coagulation and sedimentation (Fig. 2.1). In atomic absorption flame photometry total consumption burners are not used as often as in emission flame photometry. The resulting turbulent flame has generally a higher noise level than the laminar flame resulting from premixed gases. Its advantage, on the other hand, is a higher *atomization yield* (i.e. the ratio of the solution volume entering the flame to the total solution volume sprayed), because the whole sample passes through the flame (for this reason these burners are called *total consumption burners*). Although some of the bigger droplets do not evaporate

---

* See p. 32.

completely, the overall concentration of the analysed atoms in the flame gases is about 10 times higher than for the laminar flames (373). On the other hand, the possible absorption path length is relatively short. Therefore, atomizers with cloud chambers are preferred in absorption flame photometry.

Pneumatic atomizers may be constructed *concentrically* (150), i.e. with suction capillary and the pressure jet coaxial, or with the capillary and the pressure jet perpendicular.

The amount of solution sprayed depends on the capillary diameter and the gas pressure used (196). Generally, the oxidant is used as a forcing gas with some $0.9 - 1$ atmosphere excess pressure. At this pressure the velocity of the gas leaving the jet reaches the velocity of sound and any further pressure variations have only a small influence on the gas volume leaving the jet per unit time.

The bigger droplets coagulate in the cloud chamber and flow out through a siphon. Cloud chambers of different sizes and forms have been designed. According to HERRMANN and LANG (151), the suitable size depends on the total gas flow, the solution volume sprayed and the time constant of the electrical measuring device. The time necessary for reaching a steady state is naturally longer for bigger cloud chambers.

In recent years, a trend towards a small cloud chamber with a shorter path between the atomizer and the burner has been observed. With such small cloud chambers connected directly to the burner, a steady state is attained in a short time, which makes the measurement relatively fast. To secure a thorough mixing of the fuel and oxidant, the laminar streaming pattern in the cloud chamber is sometimes disturbed by so-called flow spoilers (176, 359).

The use of pneumatic atomizers, even though very simple, has several disadvantages. Their yield is relatively small (24), usually below 10%. The proportionality between the concentration of the analysed elements in the solution and in the flame is influenced by the physico-chemical properties of the solution sprayed; e.g. the viscosity, the surface tension and the vapour pressure of the solvent (98, 142). These may vary according to the total salt concentration of the solution and the presence of organic compounds especially (371). Moreover, if the salt content is too high, the salt may crystallize in the sprayer nozzle and thus influence its function. Generally, the concentration of salts in the solution should not exceed 2–3%. This level naturally depends on the construction parameters of the atomizer and may differ somewhat for the different types.

Severe changes in the atomizer performance may be caused by organic solvents. These usually have a much higher vapour pressure than water, so that the evaporation of droplets in the cloud chamber proceeds much faster, coagulation decreases and the atomization yield increases. Although the volume of the solution entering the flame is always greater than the volume of solvent which may evaporate in the corresponding gas volume at the given temperature, these two volumes are proportionally dependent (98). The atomisation yield may, therefore, be increased either by raising the volume of the gas used for spraying a definite amount of solution, by increasing the vapour pressure of the solvent through heating the forcing gas (298), or through using organic solvents with greater vapour pressures (21, 209, 280).

For total consumption burners with 100% atomization yield the influence of the physico-chemical properties of the solution sprayed should be negligible. However, this is far from true. The dispersion of the aerosol depends on the surface tension of the solution sprayed, as well as on its viscosity, which therefore influences the evaporation rate and the final concentration of free atoms in the flame. Besides this, organic solvents have a much smaller cooling effect than water with its high latent heat of evaporation, so that the temperature and all temperature dependent reactions in the flame are influenced by these properties (304, 372).

2.5 EVAPORATION IN THE FLAME

For a total consumption burner the solvent only starts to evaporate in the flame. For pre-mixed flames the greater part of the solvent has evaporated before entering the reaction zone, where the solid particles get warmed up and their evaporation starts. If the boiling point of the compound forming the solid particles lies below the flame temperature, evaporation proceeds almost immediately. This is the case with most salts of the alkali metals, copper, silver, zinc, cadmium, etc. However, if the boiling point lies above the flame temperature, the evaporation of the particles need not be complete even before leaving the flame (31).

The *evaporation rate* and, therefore, the concentration of free atoms depends on the vapour pressure at the particular flame temperature, on the total surface of the solid particles, i.e. on their number, mean size and form. The mean size in its turn depends on the size of the droplets and the concentration of salts in the solution sprayed.

Prior to evaporation various reactions may take place in the flame, so that various compounds with different vapour pressures may result. For instance, hydrated chlorides of many elements release hydrochloric acid and become oxides with considerably lower vapour pressures than the corresponding chlorides (Al, Mg). Others may release water, forming dehydrated chlorides with a much higher evaporation rate (e.g. Ca, Sr) — (294).

It is hard to estimate the proportion of a compound with a boiling point above the flame temperature which is evaporated in the flame. Many of the essential data are not available, or their values disagree considerably according to different authors. For an aerosol of calcium oxide resulting by evaporation in an acetylene-air flame of droplets with a diameter of 20 microns from a solution of 200 ppm calcium, the values given in Table 2.2 were calculated.

Table 2.2

EVAPORATION RATE OF CALCIUM OXIDE AEROSOL
$T = 2,500°K$

Time msec	% evaporated in flame
0·5	5
1	10
2	22
5	47
10	79
20	98

Full details given in the text

It is evident that the optimum working conditions are achieved if all the salts present evaporate completely. From this point of view flames with higher temperatures have some advantages. If evaporation is only partial, all the working conditions must be kept strictly constant, otherwise changes in the evaporated portion and the concentration of free atoms in the observed part of the flame may result.

2.6 REACTIONS IN THE FLAME

Even with complete evaporation of the salts in the flame the proportionality between the concentration in the solution and the number of free atoms in the flame gases is influenced by chemical reactions, which may shift the particular equilibria between free atoms and some other forms of existence of the element whose concentration is to be determined. From the analytical point of view the most important of these reactions are the *dissociation*

$$MX \; \rightleftarrows \; M + X$$

and the *ionization*

$$M \; \rightleftarrows \; M^+ + e \, .$$

Here, M represents a metal atom, X the anion and e a free electron. Each reaction, being an equilibrium, is characterized by a temperature dependent equilibrium constant which is a function of the concentrations of all reactants present. At a certain distance from the reaction zone, the flame may be considered as being in thermal equilibrium, so that all reactions may be described by equilibrium constants for the appropriate temperature. For pre-mixed flames this temperature is well-defined. In turbulent flames, droplets of unevaporated solvent enter the flame, and so thermal and concentration gradients near the droplet surfaces result, so that a characterization by equilibrium constants is only an approximation (304).

The concentration of the different particles appearing in the expression for the equilibrium constants may be expressed by the number of particles in an unit volume, or by their partial pressure. The mutual relation

NORTHWEST MISSOURI STATE
UNIVERSITY LIBRARY
MARYVILLE, MISSOURI 64468

between these two is given approximately by the equation

$$P = nkT,$$

where P is the partial pressure, n the number of particles per unit volume, k the BOLTZMANN constant and T the absolute temperature. According to the units used, the dimension of the equilibrium constant may differ. Further, we shall use partial pressure in atmospheres.

The particular constants for dissociation and ionization are expressed by the equation

$$K_{diss.} = P_M P_X / P_{MX}$$

and

$$K_{ion.} = P_{M^+} P_e / P_M$$

where P is the partial pressure of the component indicated by the suffix and K the equilibrium constant. Both constants, i.e. the dissociation and the ionization constants, depend on temperature. Their value increases with increasing temperature, i.e. both the degree of dissociation and ionization increase. The temperature dependence of the ionization constant is given by the SAHA *equation*

$$\log K_{ion.} = \frac{-5,040 E_i}{T} + \frac{5}{2} \log T - 6 \cdot 5 \log \frac{2 g_{M^+}}{g_M}, \qquad (2.1)$$

where E_i is the ionization energy in eV, T the temperature in °K, g the statistical weight* of the particles indicated in the suffix. The last member on the right hand side of the equation (2.1) has a value $\log 1 = 0$ for the alkali metals and $\log 4 = 0 \cdot 6$ for the alkali earth metals.

For the temperature dependence of the dissociation constant the following relation holds

$$\log K_{diss.} = \frac{5,040 D}{T} + \frac{5}{2} \log T - 1 \cdot 585 + 1 \cdot 5 \log \frac{g_M g_X}{g_{MX}} + \log \frac{U_M U_X}{U_{MX}},$$
$$(2.2)$$

where D is the dissociation energy in eV, g the statistical weight of the ground states of the particles marked by the suffix and U the partition functions*) of the different particles at a given temperature. As may be

---

* See, for example, MOORE: *Physical Chemistry*, Longmans Green, 352.

seen, the value of the dissociation constant is also influenced by the rotational and vibrational energies of the molecule and these may differ for the different types of molecules. However, the main and decisive influence again belongs to the dissociation energy D. Values of dissociation energies of oxides and the ionization energies for most of the elements are given in Table 9.13 at the end of the book.

The dissociation and ionization equilibria are interrelated so that a calculation of the partial pressure due to the particular constituents is rather complicated. As an example let us consider the equilibria taking place after introducing an alkali metal halide into the flame. The particular reactions taking place may be expressed as follows:

$$K_{MX} = \frac{P_M P_X}{P_{MX}}; \quad K_M = \frac{P_{M^+} P_e}{P_M}; \quad K_X = \frac{P_X P_e}{P_{X^-}}.$$

They are further bound by the condition of electrical neutrality

$$P_{M^+} = P_e + P_{X^-}$$

and the condition for the constant total concentration of the metal and halogen atoms.

$$P_{\Sigma M} = P_{MX} + P_M + P_{M^+}; \quad P_{\Sigma X} = P_{MX} + P_X + P_{X^-}.$$

From these six equations the six variables may be calculated.

In this description, reactions with the flame gases such as, for example, the formation of hydroxides, have been disregarded. In the simple example when only one alkali halide is present in the solution sprayed, dissociation and ionization depend on its concentration in the flame. This is given by the concentration in the solution, by the atomization yield and the volume of flame gases. Although these parameters may vary considerably under various working conditions, the relations found by different authors disagree by more than one decimal order. For pre-mixed flames with cloud chambers the relation

$$P_{\Sigma M} = C \cdot 10^{-4} \tag{2.3}$$

may be taken as a rough approximation (288). In eq. (2.3) $P_{\Sigma M}$ is the partial pressure of the metal in all its different forms of existence, and

C is its molar concentration in the solution. For total consumption burners the constant is about one order higher

$$P_{\Sigma M} = C . 10^{-3} . \tag{2.4}$$

For exact calculations, the relation between the concentration in the solution and in the flame must be determined experimentally (158, 161).

Table 2.3

THE COMPOSITION OF SOME FLAMES IN ATMOSPHERES

Compound present	*Type of flame*			
	Acetylene-air	*Acetylene-oxygen*	*Hydrogen-air*	*Hydrogen-oxygen*
CO_2	0·116	0·136	—	—
CO	0·039	0·315	—	—
H_2O	0·069	0·107	0·32	0·545
O_2	0·016	0·125	0·004	0·047
O	0·0022	0·099	0·0005	0·033
H_2	0·0038	0·034	0·0173	0·154
H	0·0019	0·060	0·002	0·082
OH	0·0095	0·110	0·0097	0·134
NO	0·01	—	0·002	—
N_2	0·731	—	0·645	—

When the anionic constituent of the dissociating species is simultaneously a constituent of the flame gases, a special case of dissociation equilibrium results. The anion component of the flame gases is present in a 'concentration many times higher than its concentration in the injected solution. It may, therefore, be included in the equilibrium constant and the equilibrium condition simplifies to an equation expressing a constant ratio of the dissociated and undissociated forms of the metal

$$P_M/P_{MY} = K'$$

(where Y is the anion concerned).

The calculations are then somewhat easier. In the acetylene-air flame this component may be oxygen or the hydroxyl radical. The formation of hydrides is less important from the analytical point of view.

One of the greatest difficulties in flame photometry is the *formation of oxides* of the elements to be analysed. In these cases either high temperature flames must be used to shift the dissociation in favour of the free atoms or the partial pressure of oxygen in the flame must be diminished either by increasing the fuel flow (188) or by using organic solvents (128, 281). A reducing incandescent flame results, in which the degree of dissociation of the oxides is increased. Due to diffusion of atmospheric oxygen into the flame the reducing zone is limited and adjacent to the reaction zone.

2.7 ABSORPTION TUBES

For elements with free atoms of sufficiently long lifetime the sensitivity of determination may be increased by using an absorption tube (120) placed along the optical axis (i. e. the line along which the light beam is directed). The flame is introduced into this so that the flame gases are kept in the absorption path for a much longer time (see Fig. 2.2). The total absorption path length is determined by the tube length which may

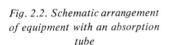
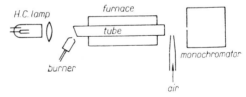

Fig. 2.2. Schematic arrangement of equipment with an absorption tube

be up to 100 cm. However, the sensitivity of determination is proportional to this length only in a limited interval (189, 390). If the tubes are too long, the lifetime* of the free atoms is exceeded and a further increase in the absorption path length will bring about no enhancement of absorption. The optimum tube length depends on the flow velocity of gases

* Lifetime under the influence of ionizing agents, etc., not optical lifetime.

and on the lifetime of the free atoms. This lifetime is naturally given by the composition and temperature of the flame gases. This may be seen on Fig. 2.3 where the absorbance of several elements (measured perpendicularly to the tube axis) is plotted against the distance from the tube end. For elements with a long lifetime (e.g. Ag, Pb) the absorbance falls off very slowly, whereas for elements which form oxides more

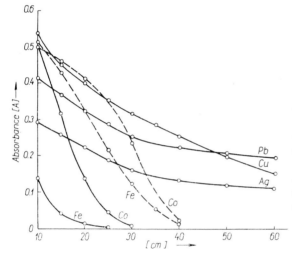

Fig. 2.3. Variation of the absorbance of some elements at different distance from the entrance end of an absorption tube (339)

Air flow 2·3 l/min, hydrogen flow, full line 6·1 l/min, interrupted line 12·5 l/min

easily (e.g. Fe, Co) the absorption falls off relatively steeply and may be influenced by increasing the fuel flow because less oxidation then occurs (334). Excessively long tubes should not be employed, because unfavourable effects, such as light scattering and molecular absorption may become a nuisance.

The gas mixtures used with absorption tubes depend on the temperature the tube material can withstand. So far steel, silica glass (Vycor), alumina and some other temperature resistant ceramics have been used (see Table 2.4). Silica tubes are very resistant to thermal shocks. But as they also act as light guides, the radiation flux falling on the entrance slit of the detector system depends on the reflectivity of the inner walls of the absorption tube. If we now spray a solution with a higher salt content, the salt may precipitate on the walls changing their reflectivity. Therefore the signal corresponding to a 100% transmission steadily changes. This makes the measurement difficult, if not impossible. Ceramic tubes are free from this trouble, but care must be taken to avoid cracking them

Table 2.4
REVIEW OF ABSORPTION TUBE APPLICATIONS

Flame	Material	Length cm	Diameter cm	Element	Sensitivity ppm	Reference
coal-gas-air	steel	30 – 50	1·5 – 1·8	Cu	0·09	
	brass	T-shaped		Ag	0·058	
				Au	0·042	
				Cd	0·02	390
hydrogen-air	silica glass "Vycor"	90	1	Cd	0·0004	
				Zn	0·0006	120
				Mg	0·005	
				Cu	0·007	
				Co	0·013	
				Ni	0·016	
hydrogen-air	aluminium	25	1·5	Zn	0·002	121
hydrogen-oxygen	stainless steel	25 T-shaped	1·3	Hg	0·2	115
hydrogen-oxygen	silica glass	40	1	Ag	0·008	189
				Au	0·05	
				Bi	0·1	
				Cd	0·001	
				Cu	0·005	
				Mg	0·001	
				Pb	0·002	
				Sb	0·1	
				Te	0·02	
				Tl	0·05	
				Zn	0·001	
hydrogen-oxygen	silica glass	40	0·9	Sn	0·025	13

Table 2.4 continued

Flame	Material	Length cm	Diameter cm	Element	Sensitiv- ity ppm	Reference
hydrogenair	silica glass	60	1	Cd	0·001	333
				Ag	0·004	334
				Co	0·015	
				Cu	0·007	
				Fe	0·015	
				Pb	0·03	
hydrogen-air	silica glass	100	1·6	Pb	0·015	278
hydrogen-air	Pyrolan glass	45	1·7	Au	0·01	
				Pd	0·01	292
				Rh	0·02	
				Pt	0·5	
hydrogen-air	Pyrolan	45	1·7	Ag	0·002	
				Cd	0·001	294B
				Pb	0·05	
hydrogen-oxygen	silica glass	T-shaped		Pb	0·013	72
hydrogen-oxygen	silica glass	T-shaped		Cd	0·002	272A
				Cu	0·008	
				Zn	0·002	

when warming up. With metallic tubes the danger of corrosion may be prohibitive.

The hottest flame so far used with silica tubes has been the hydrogen-oxygen flame, which has a temperature of about 2,500°C. The part of the absorption tube where the flame touches its walls must be cooled by a stream of air (13). Total consumption burners ensuring a higher concentration of the sample in the flame gases are usually used. The flame may either be introduced into the tube in the middle and leave it at both ends (this is the T-shaped tube), or it may enter by one end and leave it at the other (see Fig. 2.2). Recently the latter has been more often used, because its construction and handling are simpler. To protect the other parts of the equipment from the hot gases, these must be either exhausted (120) or blown away by a protective stream of air (13, 189).

The question of the optimum tube diameter is far from being definitively solved. The tube diameter usually chosen is between one and two centimetres. A smaller diameter makes optical alignment difficult, whereas too large a diameter may have an unfavourable influence on the stability of absorption. The whole tube must be uniformly filled with flame gases and this is naturally more difficult to ensure for tubes of larger diameter. The resulting absorption (i.e. the sensitivity of determination), depends markedly on the fuel to oxidant flow ratio. For tubes with a larger diameter the optimum fuel flow is higher, because more air from the atmosphere is carried with it (292).

One of the unpleasant properties of absorption tubes is their "memory" effect due to precipitation on the walls, etc. After spraying solutions with a high concentration of the element to be determined, the tube must be cleaned by spraying with distilled water, or more preferably diluted hydrochloric acid. This "memory" effect depends on the pressure of the appropriate element. It is small for both very volatile elements (e.g. Zn, Cd), which do not condense on the tube walls, and for very involatile elements which once condensed can hardly be volatilized again (e.g. Pt, Rh). For some elements the "memory" effect depends on the acid present. For instance, iron has a big "memory" effect in hydrochloric solutions but a negligible one in nitric solutions (334).

The second unfavourable factor with absorption tubes is the considerable background absorption, many times higher than in normal flames. The reason for this is that the absorption path length is considerably longer and the temperature generally lower, so that evaporation and dissociation may not be complete. In some cases molecular absorption of some compounds has been observed (190, 191). Alkali metal halides manifest strong molecular absorption maxima corresponding to incomplete dissociation processes. Sulphuric acid also exhibits a strong maximum below 200 nm and a less pronounced one near 280 nm. Both these effects must be corrected for by subtracting the absorbance due to light scattering or molecular absorption, from the absorbance of the element measured.

The use of absorption tubes for the determination of different elements is summed up in Table 2.4. Although so far it is not a common technique, it evidently can bring a considerable sensitivity enhancement for many elements. To this end, absorption tubes of simple construction and easy operation will be required.

2.8 OTHER MEANS FOR THE PRODUCTION OF ATOMIC VAPOURS

For atomization of the samples, the thermal energy of electric discharges may also be exploited. In such devices the dissociation of refractory oxides may be more complete, both because the temperature attainable is higher and because oxygen may be completely excluded from the absorption medium.

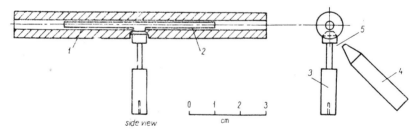

Fig. 2.4. Graphite furnace of Lvov (212)
1 — graphite tube, 2 — tantalum foil, 3 — graphite electrode supporting the sample, 4 — auxiliary electrode, 5 — arc discharge

An electric arc in a graphite furnace is used for the evaporation of the sample by Lvov (211, 212). It consists of a 5 – 10 cm long graphite tube with an inner diameter between 2 and 3 mm electrically heated to 2,000 – 3,000°K. A graphite electrode with the sample on its upper surface is inserted into a hole at the central part of the graphite tube (see Fig. 2.4) and is heated up by a high current d.c. arc (40 – 60 amperes) burning between this supporting and an auxiliary electrode. The sample is thus very quickly evaporated into the graphite tube. To prevent losses of the sample vapour by diffusion through the walls of the graphite tube it is lined with a tantalum foil. The graphite tube must be long enough to ensure that the volume of the sample vapour does not exceed the volume of the tube, otherwise losses of the sample through the open ends would take place before all the sample has been vaporized. Also, the evaporation must proceed faster than the diffusion through the open ends. Diffusion may be slowed down somewhat by increasing the pressure in the chamber in which the whole equipment is enclosed.

The measurement proceeds as follows. The supporting electrodes with the analysed samples are put into the chamber. This is then closed, evacuated and filled with an inert gas. The current heating the graphite tube is switched on and after the required temperature is reached the supporting electrode is inserted in the appropriate opening and the auxiliary d.c. arc automatically ignited for $3-4$ sec. During that time absorption in the graphite tube is recorded. After reaching a maximum, the absorption decreases due to diffusion of atoms from the graphite tube.

This method has a very high absolute sensitivity reaching down to $10-12$ gm. This is comprehensible, taking into account that all the atoms present take part in absorbing light, whereas with flames it is only about one in every 20,000. However, the relative (concentration) sensitivity is not very different from that of the flame method, because the size of the sample which may be analysed is very limited (only some $20-40$ μgm). The result naturally depends on the size of the sample, so that it must be measured precisely onto the supporting electrode with a micropipette. The precision, attaining only some $5-10\%$, is generally lower than with the flame method.

However, for the analysis of extremely small samples this method is unmatched and it will certainly find broader use in the future. Another advantage is that the results are almost independent on the overall composition of the samples. For instance, aluminium and zinc contents were determined in different alloys, metals, acids and hydroxides, using a single working curve for all these materials (253, 254).

The plasma of an electric discharge may also be used directly as the absorbing medium. Thus, ROBINSON (284) sprayed a solution into a spark discharge to observe aluminium absorption lines. An analytically useful device using induction coupled plasmas has been described by WENDT and FASSEL (355, 356). FRIED (118) explored the possibilities of plasma jets for the refractory elements.

An absorption medium may also be prepared by cathode sputtering, as in the glow discharge of a hollow cathode. The free atoms are only relatively slowly lost by diffusion from the cathode and the absolute sensitivity attained may be relatively high. On the other hand, cathode sputtering is a rather selective process depending on the overall composition of the sample. This makes standardization somewhat difficult.

Cathode sputtering has been used by GATEHOUSE and WALSH in a sputtering chamber (123). This is a stainless steel tube with silica windows on both ends and connected to a vacuum circulation system. In its central part the sample is coaxially fixed in the form of a hollow cylinder. The chamber is flushed with argon and a glow discharge is switched on with the sample as the cathode. This sputtering chamber has been successfully used for the determination of silver and phosphorus concentrations in copper, and silicon in aluminium and steel (352). Unfortunately, the samples must be machined into a cylinder which makes the whole process complicated.

GOLEB and BRODY (136) tried water-cooled demountable hollow cathode tubes. The sample solutions were evaporated on the inner walls of an aluminium hollow cathode, this was then mounted, connected to the vacuum circulation system and placed in the optical axis. With this device they were able to detect 1 μgm of sodium, magnesium, calcium, beryllium and silicon. The mutual influence of the different elements was considerable. By increasing the electric current the sensitivity is enhanced due to a more intense sputtering. However, the time of constant absorption is shorter. A current of 100 mA is, therefore, recommended (136).

IVANOV (8) was able to detect even less (i.e. 0·01 μgm of copper and 0·1 μgm of calcium) using a graphite hollow cathode tube. He showed that the sensitivity may be increased by decreasing the mass of the cathode. The highest sensitivity is attained by evaporating the sample onto a thin molybdenum wire, which is then placed coaxially in the hollow cathode (171).

CHAPTER 3

LIGHT SOURCES

Light sources for any absorption measurement should have a high stability and a high emissive power of radiation, so that the sensitivity of the detection system need not be overstrained. For atomic absorption some further requirements have been derived in Chapter 1. Namely, that the light source should emit intense, narrow, non-self-absorbed resonance lines, without continuous background and without any further lines in the monochromator pass band measured. If these conditions are not fulfilled, the sensitivity of determination decreases and the working curves are bent. Taking requirements into account, low pressure discharges with small broadening effects seem most promising.

3.1 HOLLOW CATHODE DISCHARGE TUBES

So far the best results for almost all elements have been attained with hollow cathode lamps. These light sources have been used since the beginning of this century for studies of atomic spectra. They were usually connected to a vacuum system providing circulation of some inert gas during operation. Because a vacuum circulating system is too bulky for atomic absorption, closed, sealed-off hollow cathode tubes are prevalently used nowadays. This type of hollow cathode lamp has been developed by CROSSWHITE et al. (75) for the interferometric measurement of iron lines.

The hollow lamp is formed from an evacuated vessel, into which the electrodes are sealed, filled with an inert gas (see Fig. 3.1). The cathode is a hollow cylinder with an inner diameter of less than 10 mm. The position and form of the anode are largely irrelevant. Opposite to the cavity of the hollow cathode is placed an optical window transmitting the required radiation (i. e. quartz windows for wavelengths below 370 nm). If sufficient voltage is applied between the two electrodes, a *glow discharge* starts. At a suitable pressure it concentrates in the hollow of the cathode and attains current densities several times greater than those of a normal glow discharge.

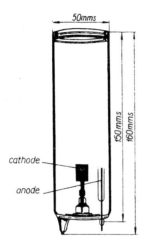

Fig. 3.1. Typical hollow cathode lamp

The *mechanism of the discharge* is usually explained as follows: electrons leaving the cathode due to the applied voltage collide with atoms of the filling gas and cause their ionization. The positively charged ions gain kinetic energy from the potential difference, fall and strike the cathode surface, knocking out atoms from its crystal lattice. The sputtered atoms become excited in the hollow where an enlarged concentration of the metal atoms is maintained and therefore also their emission is greater. At present it is not quite clear how the atoms become excited in this region. It is generally assumed that the excitation proceeds by collisions of the second kind (with the excited atoms and ions of the inert gas) or by direct electron impact.

The cathode should always be made from the element whose spectrum the lamp is to emit. Most often *pure metals* are used. Precious metals may be inserted in the form of a foil into a cathode made from a more common metal, which may be, for example, copper, aluminium or iron (207). The metal may also be deposited by electrolysis.

At normal operating currents the cathode may attain some 300°C. For metals with low melting points, alloys with higher melting points are preferable, unless extremely low operating currents can be used, so as not to exceed the melting point of the pure metal. For elements with very low vapour pressures, the brightness of such lamps is often insufficient. It is, therefore, better to place the low melting element in a cup-shaped cathode (60). During operation the metal may melt without damage to the lamp.

The material of supporting electrode should have a higher work function than the element under consideration, to minimize the current flow between the exterior of the cathode and the anode. It should be wetted by the molten element but should not form an alloy with it. Cup-shaped hollow cathodes made from tantalum and titanium have been recommended for gallium and indium respectively (246).

Hollow cathode tubes as absorption sources have been used for isotopic analyses of lithium (137) and uranium (138).

Thermal vaporization of elements to produce free atoms may also be accomplished by heating with an intense pulse of light from a discharge lamp, discharged through a capacitor (1,000 joules of light can be produced in this way). Such a device has been described by NELSON and KUEBLER (249, 250). If the dimension of the sample with the supporting strip does not exceed some 100 microns the temperature may rise up to several thousand degrees Centigrade in a single flash. The resulting burst of atomic vapour has a duration of about 1 msec.

A laser pulse has also been tried. In this case the lifetime of atomic vapour is only 20−100 msec (144). Both sets of equipment using light pulses are too complicated for analytical use, as the absorption spectra must be recorded over a very short period.

Generally it may be concluded that all these methods other than flames for producing atomic vapour have two main advantages. Firstly, they make analysis of minute samples possible. This may be useful when the samples are very precious or radioactive. The second advantage is that they make work in closed systems possible, which again may be appreciated for work with radioactive materials. By excluding oxygen from the atmosphere, elements having their lines in the SCHUMANN region (where oxygen absorbs strongly) can also be measured. Apart from these advantages none of the described methods can compete with flames in simplicity and ease of operation.

Hollow cathode lamps made from *alloys* have one further advantage, in that the lamp need not be changed when passing over from one element to another. However, if the two components do not form a true intermetallic compound, one component is usually sputtered preferentially, so that its spectrum emitted by the lamp gradually weakens and the lamp degenerates into a one element lamp. This is the case with zinc in brass hollow cathode lamps. If a true intermetallic compound is formed, as, for example, calcium and magnesium (219), no preferential sputtering takes place. Such possibilities are, however, limited.

Hollow cathode lamps with several cathodes from different metals (173) generally do not perform well, nor do lamps with hollow cathodes composed of several rings of different metals (227). Operating conditions with these lamps must be held strictly constant, otherwise variations in the intensities of the particular elements occur. Powder metallurgy presents a better possibility. The metal powders may be mixed and pressed into a cathode. Because the size of individual grains is large on an atomic scale, no preferential vaporization takes place. Thus, e.g. hollow cathode lamps for Cu + Mn, Cu + Cr and Ni + Co + Fe + + Cu + Ca + Mn (300) have been prepared. The combination of elements should be carefully selected so as not to cause interference between emitted spectra.

3.2 RADIATION FROM HOLLOW CATHODE LAMPS

The radiation flux density of the hollow cathode lamps depends on two processes, the *cathode sputtering* and the *excitation in the negative glow*. In normal hollow cathode lamps both processes are interrelated. By increasing the electric current both the sputtering and the excitation are enhanced. However, if too high a concentration of free atoms in the vapour state is reached, self-absorption of the resonance lines takes place, which, as has been shown in Chapter 1, lowers the sensitivity of determination and causes bending of the working curves.

Self-absorption depends also on the size and form of the hollow cathode. Outside the cavity where a lower temperature reigns, absorption is particularly severe and even self-reversal of the resonance lines may take place. The form securing lowest self-absorption seems to be a hollow sphere with a small exit hole (346) to restrict the amount of metal vapour leaving the cavity.

The sputtering process depends primarily on the kinetic energy and number of inert gas ions striking the cathode. This sputtering is always smaller for the light gases than for the heavy ones.* Thus, with helium and neon, even if the electric current and therefore also the number of ions striking the surface is increased, the sputtering may not reach a level at which self-absorption manifests itself, and the only result is that the excitation process in the hollow cathode is enhanced.

For a definite gas and pressure the radiation flux density (J) of a spectral line from a hollow cathode lamp depends on the electric current according to the empirical formula (75)

$$J = \text{const}\, j^n$$

where j is the electric current and n an exponent determined by the material of the cathode, the filler gas and the line measured.

Comparing the radiation flux density of resonance lines for a number of elements, using *different inert gases* at various pressures it has been found (49) that for less volatile elements (Fe, Mo, Ni, Co, Cr, Cu, Ti) neon at a pressure of 3 torr secures a greater brightness than argon. Argon at a pressure of $1 - 1 \cdot 5$ torr has been found better for Al, Ca and Mg. For the most volatile elements (Bi, Cd, Pb, Sn, Zn), an increase in brightness of radiation with decreasing pressure has been observed for all inert gases. Generally, increasing the lamp current of argon filled lamps often produces a lower sensitivity of measurement (184, 346) and helium or neon filled lamps are recommended.

The choice of the filler gas is also sometimes influenced by the spectrum emitted. Thus, for example, the strongest chromium line Cr 357·9 nm may interfere with the argon line at 357·7 nm (182) and, therefore, neon

---

* This can be understood if the sputtering is considered as "billiard-ball" like collisions, between two particles of dissimilar mass.

would be preferred in this case. Similarly argon emits a line at 217·14 nm near the strongest lead line at 217·00 nm. If the two lines are not resolved the sensitivity is naturally diminished. Increasing the electric current of the hollow cathode lamp may then bring a sensitivity increase because the lead line intensity increases more rapidly than the argon one. However, the use of too high a current shortens the lifetime of the lamp. If neon is used as a filler gas with a lead hollow cathode lamp, the Pb line at 217·00 nm is preferred (313). The filler gas may easily be recognized by the colour of the discharge. A blue discharge indicates argon, an orange-red one neon. In general, the neon spectrum offers most interferences in the wavelength regions 330 − 370 and 500 − 650 nm, whereas argon does so in the 400 − 500 nm region.

3.3 HIGH BRIGHTNESS HOLLOW CATHODE LAMP

Much better performance hollow cathode emission may be attained if the two processes, i.e. cathode sputtering and excitation, are independent and controlled by separate electric discharges. This is realized in the so-called high brightness or high intensity hollow cathode lamps (327), in which a *pair of auxiliary electrodes* is added and an auxiliary boosting discharge burns between them. The glow discharge

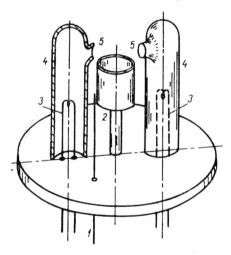

Fig. 3.2. Electrode assembly of a high-brightness hollow cathode lamp 1 — anode, 2 — cathode, 3 — booster electrodes, 4 — insulating shield forcing the auxiliary discharge to take place between the openings 5

between the hollow cathode and the anode controls only the sputtering process producing the metal vapour. The free atoms leaving the cavity of the cathode by diffusion form a cloud of free atoms outside its mouth. The auxiliary electrodes with a low voltage arc burning between them are placed in either side of this cloud. The metal atoms become excited in the positive column of this boosting discharge, and its current may be up to 300–400 mA. The auxiliary electrodes are insulated and a small opening forces the auxiliary discharge to pass directly before the mouth of the hollow cathode (see Fig. 3.2). To ensure a low voltage drop across the boosting discharge, oxide coated tungsten electrodes with a low work function are used. The voltage drop is so small (20–30 V) that the energy available is insufficient for excitation of ion lines or even of the inert gas lines. The resonance lines of the metal are, on the other hand, enhanced up to a hundred times. The major part of all radiation emitted is, therefore, concentrated in the resonance lines. This is very important for elements with line rich spectra (Fe, Co, Ni, Mo) where the isolation of resonance lines would require monochromators with a high resolving power. Otherwise the working curves are more or less curved, due to neighbouring interfering lines. Because these interfering non-absorbing lines are suppressed with high brightness lamps, the working curves are straightened.

3.4 OPERATION OF HOLLOW CATHODE LAMPS

The stability of the spectral output of a hollow cathode lamp is given by the stability of the power supply. Because the current is almost independent of the voltage applied (the current-voltage characteristic of a glow discharge runs almost parallel to the current axis), the power supply must be either current stabilized or, if a more common voltage stabilized power supply is used, a series resistance is necessary to limit the current. The voltage drop on the electrodes of a hollow cathode lamp is entirely dependent on the cathode material and the filler gas. The series resistance should be between 1 and 10 kΩ. The higher its value, the better the current stabilization, but a higher resistance naturally requires a higher voltage supply. For most work a voltage stabilized supply of 500 – 1,000 V and 50 mA d. c. output is sufficient.

The spectral output of the hollow cathode lamp is approximately proportional to the discharge current. The requirements on its stability are different whether working with single beam or double beam spectrophotometers. For a single beam instrument the stability should be at least 0·25% or if possible even 0·1%. For double beam instruments, where the absorbed to unabsorbed signal ratio is measured, the requirements are less stringent and in most cases a 1% stability would be adequate. However, in special cases, namely, when the resonance line measured is strongly self-absorbed, this stability may not be sufficient.

Hollow cathode lamps are operated mostly at currents ranging between 5 and 30 mA and exceptionally up to 50 mA. The recommended and maximum operating currents are usually indicated on the lamp. The maximum operating current is limited by two factors. The increased heating of the cathode may cause melting of the material and also increased cathode sputtering shortens the lifetime of the hollow cathode lamp due to removal of the filler gas, which becomes adsorbed on the sputtered cathode material (173). This adsorption is stronger for the light inert gases, i.e. helium and neon, than for argon. Argon-filled lamps are from this point of view preferable. By increasing the lamp volume its life may be prolonged (173).

Most producers of hollow cathode lamps guarantee a *lifetime* of 5 ampere-hours, but this is considerably exceeded in most cases. By long storage of hollow cathode lamps without operation, their performance may deteriorate. A continuum is emitted and the spectrum of the cathode material is weakened. This results in a smaller signal to noise ratio. Such lamps may be restored by letting the lamp burn for a long period or by reversing the polarity for some time.

3.5 THE MANUFACTURE OF HOLLOW CATHODE LAMPS IN THE LABORATORY

In any laboratory hollow cathode lamps may be prepared with the aid of a glassblower. Their lifetime usually cannot compete with commercially produced specimens. Some metals are exceptionally hard on outgassing and the spectrum of such hollow cathode lamps then constantly deteriorates as the gases, especially hydrogen, dissolved in the metal, are released. Hydrogen emits an intense continuous spectrum in the ultraviolet region and also attenuates the spectrum of the cathode material, because it uses up part of the excitation energy available.

Therefore, some research workers recommend providing laboratory-made hollow cathode lamps with a vacuum tap and a ground glass

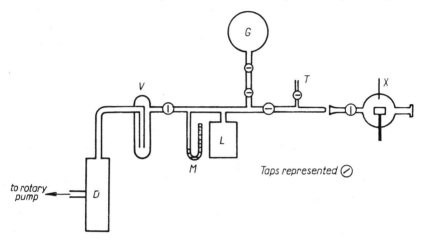

Fig. 3.3. Vacuum apparatus for filling a hollow cathode lamp: D — diffusion pump, V — cold trap, M — mercury manometer, L — McLeod gauge, G — cylinder containing the rare gas, T — air inlet when removing filled lamps, X — hollow cathode lamp

joint so that they may be easily connected to the vacuum system and reconditioned (60, 299) — (see Fig. 3.3).

The electrodes are fastened to molybdenum or tungsten rods of 2–4 mm diameter sealed into the glass. The optical window may be cemented to the tube with black wax. Care should be taken, however, because of its low melting point. For radiation below 380 nm special glass or quartz windows must be used.

The vacuum system (Fig. 3.3) used for filling the hollow cathode lamps with inert gases consists of a rotary backing pump, a two or three stage diffusion pump, a liquid air trap to prevent mercury or silicone oil from the diffusion pump contaminating the system, a suitable gauge for measuring in the 0·1–5 mm pressure range, and one or two inert gas storage flasks connected through a device regulating the amount of inert gas released. This may be done either step by step by admitting a definite small volume, or by letting the gas flow through a capillary or porous ceramic.

The processing of the lamp proceeds as follows: The lamp is connected to the vacuum system, evacuated and a test is made for possible leaks. The main tap is then closed and the spectroscopically pure inert gas is admitted into the system up to a pressure of about 3 mm of mercury. The power supply is connected to the electrodes and switched on. A discharge should start. At the beginning it may be erratic until the surface of the cathode is clean. The discharge should be operated at the highest possible current, taking care not to damage the cathode by melting the metal. After several minutes the discharge is switched off and the tube is evacuated. This procedure must be repeated several times until there is no sign of molecular spectra of hydrogen lines in the radiation emitted. Hydrogen may best be recognized by its red line at 656 nm using a simple pocket spectroscope. Some metals are relatively easy to outgas. For others (especially noble metals) the process of heating and evacuating must be repeated for many hours. The anode surface should also be cleaned by reversing the polarity of the discharge. When the cathode has been sufficiently outgassed, the lamp is filled to its optimum pressure and sealed off. At optimum pressure the hollow cathode should glow only faintly from outside and the hollow should be uniformly filled with the radiation leaving only a thin CROOKES dark space near the inner surface.

3.6 VAPOUR DISCHARGE LAMPS

For some volatile elements (i.e. Na, K, Rb, Cs, Hg, Tl, Zn, Cd) vapour discharge lamps may be used as light sources of atomic spectra (101). These are evacuated tubes into which tungsten electrodes and a small amount of the appropriate metal and some inert gas at low pressure are sealed in. They may be supplied either from the a. c. mains with a choke switched in series, or by direct current with a series resistance (see Fig. 3.4). The discharge tube is usually made of silica glass, sometimes provided with a protecting layer against corrosive alkali metal vapours. From outside, the tube is mechanically and thermally protected by a glass bulb. If ultraviolet radiation is to be transmitted (Zn, Cd, Hg), an opening must be cut into this protecting bulb.

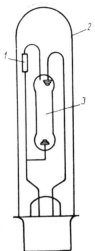

Fig. 3.4. Vapour discharge lamp
1 — thermistor used with starting electrode, 2 — thermally insulating glass envelope, 3 — vapour of substance

When sufficient potential difference is applied to the electrodes, a discharge carried by the inert gas starts. After the tube is warmed up, the sealed-in metal evaporates, takes over the discharge and provides almost all the radiation emitted. The vapour discharge lamps have a much *higher emissive power* than hollow cathode lamps. On the other hand the resonance lines are much broader, because their profile is usually distorted by self-absorption and for zinc and cadmium they even manifest distinct self-reversal (295). They are used only for the alkali metals and mercury.

Because of the much higher radiation flux density provided by the vapour discharge lamps the signal to noise ratio may be better than for hollow cathode tubes (220, 310). The performance of individual lamps may vary considerably according to the amount of the metal sealed in as this determines the degree of *self-absorption* (342). Therefore, if possible, the lamps used for atomic absorption work should be specially selected. The current supplied should be set at the lowest possible value securing a stable discharge. Although currents above 1 A are quite often required by the producer, usually 0·3–0·5 A should be used for atomic absorption spectrometry. The lines emitted are then less self-absorbed and higher sensitivity is attained.

3.7 HIGH-FREQUENCY ELECTRODELESS DISCHARGE TUBES

Other possible sources of atomic spectra are the high-frequency electrodeless discharge tubes. Recent progress in their development and improvement in their performance make it possible for them to successfully compete with hollow cathode lamps. For highly volatile elements having resonance lines at very short wavelengths (e.g. Se, Te) electrodeless discharge tubes may prove especially superior because of their considerably higher brightness. Hollow cathode lamps of these elements must be operated at very low currents, otherwise their lifetime is too short. At low currents, the emitted spectrum is weak and the radiation is further absorbed by the flame gases. The resulting radiation flux measured may be too low for precise photometric measurements.

High-frequency electrodeless discharge tubes are constructed either as silica glass cylinders of about 1 cm diameter and several centimetres long (275), or as spheres with a diameter of about 1·5 cm (38, 172). A small amount of the particular element and some inert gas (argon, xenon or krypton) at a pressure of 0·5–1·5 mm mercury is sealed in. The inert gas is used to ignite the discharge.* If no gas is added the metal must be evaporated first by external heating.

High-frequency electrodeless discharge tubes may be prepared for elements having a vapour pressure in the range 10^{-3}–1 mm mercury at the temperature attainable (8). For less volatile elements (e.g. Cu, Th) volatile compounds, usually halides, may be used instead of pure metals. High-frequency electrodeless discharge tubes for Zn, Cd, Hg, Ga, In, Tl, Sn, Pb, As, Sb, Bi, Se, Te and even Be, Mg, Ca, Sr and Mn apart from Na, K, Cs have been produced. Tubes with different combinations of elements may also be easily prepared.

The greatest problem with high-frequency electrodeless discharge

---

* It also helps to maintain it with collisions of the second kind.

tubes is to secure a stable discharge in the lamp and a stable spectral output. The tube walls must have a sufficiently high temperature to prevent condensation of the metal. The whole tube should be shielded from undefined air draughts to keep the temperature of the tube walls constant. Usually a temperature gradient is maintained, so that the metal is partly condensed in the colder part out of the main discharge region (38).

High-frequency electrodeless discharge tubes have been excited with microwave frequencies around 2,450 MHz or with radio frequencies. In the latter case the tube is placed between two poles of a radio-frequency generator (38, 172). The frequency should be between 30 and 100 MHz, its lowest value is determined by the size of the tube. The generator supply must be stabilized, since the tube impedance has a negative coefficient of resistance. Because of *skin effect* the discharge tends to concentrate near the tube walls. The light emitted, therefore, does not, as in vapour discharge lamps, pass through a layer of cold vapour where self-reversal takes place. Thus the main advantage of high-frequency electrodeless discharge tubes, next to high brightness and an almost unlimited lifetime is a small self-absorption. High-frequency electrodeless tubes are commercially produced by the Ophthos Instrument Co. in the USA, as well as in the USSR. Laboratory manufacture of these discharge tubes and the construction of suitable power supplies is described (38, 172).* For microwave excitation the discharge tube is placed into the discharge cavity of a generator, the discharge is initiated with a vacuum-tester and the cavity with the tube tuned. The high-frequency generator Microtron 200 produced by Electro-Medical Supplies (Great Britain) has successfully been used. It may be expected that high-freqency electrodeless discharge tubes will be more often used in the future in connection with atomic fluorescence spectrometry.

3.8 THE FLAME AS A SOURCE

The use of a flame, into which a relatively strong solution of the particular element is sprayed, as a light source, has also been described by several

---

* See also: V. B. GERARD, *J. Sc. Inst.*, **39**, 217 (1962).
  W. BERDOWSKI, *App. Optics*, **6** (10), 1683 (1967).

authors. But in all cases this was used only as an easily accessible substitute for other more sophisticated light sources not available for the elements required. Thus, a flame source was used in the first work of ALKEMADE and MILATZ (14), for isotopic analysis of lithium (217) and for checking the absorption lines of some rare earths (306).

For completeness' sake, the use of a spark discharge as a light source should also be mentioned (320).

3.9 CONTINUOUS SOURCES

Sources emitting continuous spectra may also be used. Their main advantage are high brightness, high stability, the possibility of using a single source for all the elements, which would bring considerable savings in acquisition costs and the possibility of easily measuring several elements simultaneously (226A). Unfortunately, these attractive attributes are more than compensated for by the disadvantages. Instruments with very high resolving power would be needed, unless a considerable loss in sensitivity is incurred. With commercially produced monochromators the sensitivity of determination may be decreased by a factor of between 30 and 100 (127).

So far continuous sources in combination with photographic detection have been used for estimating the sensitivities of different lines and different elements (23) and for the measurement of some elements in relatively high concentrations (133, 169, 170).

As sources, tungsten iodide lamps (109), high pressure xenon lamps (110, 226A) and hydrogen lamps (133, 169, 170) have been tried. In cases when the appropriate line sources available do not have an adequate performance (as until recently was the case with hollow cathode lamps for some rare earths), the results with continuous sources may be commensurable (111). But with the introduction of better hollow cathode lamps this situation will probably not be maintained much longer (28). Although, because of their universal application, continuous sources will probably be exploited even in the future.

CHAPTER 4

ISOLATION AND DETECTION
OF RADIATION

4.1 GENERAL

The analytical line must be isolated from the radiation emitted by the light source, passed through the absorbing medium and its radiation flux measured with a light detector. In atomic absorption, unlike emission spectrophotometry, the absorbing medium must be placed before the dispersing unit, which *eliminates radiation of all other wavelengths.* Although it might also be eliminated by modulation of the signal, this would raise the detector noise.

The *spectral band-width* required depends on the spectrum of the light source. If the light source emits only the resonance line measured, no spectral isolation is required. This situation is approached when using vapour discharge lamps of some alkali metals which emit up to 90% of their radiation energy in the resonance doublet (8). If, on the other hand, the light source emits in a whole wavelength region (i.e. when using continuous sources), the requirements on the isolation are raised beyond the possibilities of common monochromators and a consequent decrease of the sensitivity of measurement results. In practice, the situation is usually somewhere between these two extremes.

For alkali metals using discharge lamps, only colour or interference filters need be used. Several such simple instruments have been described in the literature (216, 353). Also they may be easily mounted in the laboratory by adding vapour discharge lamps to a flame photometer. If the concentration of the alkali metal determined is not too high, a d.c. measuring system may even be used, because the radiation flux from the discharge lamp is considerably higher than that emitted by the flame.

However, the main advantages of atomic absorption manifest themselves only when using monochromators. In general, the resolving power required is smaller than for emission flame photometry, because only the isolation of the analytical line from the other lines emitted is neccessary. For most elements this is a relatively easy task.

4.2 MONOCHROMATORS

The construction and function of monochromators may be found in numerous books on absorption spectrophotometry and flame photometry (3, 7, 9). Here, we shall only briefly mention the properties of monochromators important from the analytical point of view.

For analytical work in atomic absorption the most important factor is the *width of the pass band* isolated by the monochromator. It depends

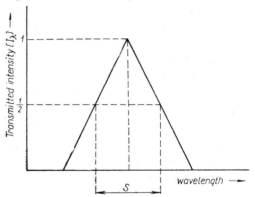

Fig. 4.1. Slit function of an ideal monochromator
s — spectral slit width

on the width of the entrance and exit slits, which are usually set to be equal, and on the dispersion of the monochromator. If continuous radiation falls on the entrance slit, after passing through the mono-chromator the radiation exhibits a distribution of energies according to wavelength. This distribution, called the *slit function*, can be represented for slits which are not too narrow, by an isosceles triangle with its peak at the wavelength chosen. The whole pass band is characterized by the width of this triangle at half its maximum value and is usually called the *spectral slit widths*. The monochromator, therefore, transmits radiation in the range of $\lambda + s$ and $\lambda - s$, where λ is the wavelength set and s the spectral slit width (see Fig. 4.1).

By closing the slit its spectral width decreases. It cannot be reduced below a certain value, given mainly by diffraction of the light and by faults in the instrument optics. For very good instruments this smallest spectral slit width may even be under 0·01 nm. It depends mainly on the theoretical resolving power of the dispersing element (i.e. the prism or grating) of the monochromator.

The performance of monochromators is sometimes characterized directly by their *theoretical resolving power*

$$R = \lambda/d\lambda .$$

Here, $d\lambda$ is the smallest wavelength difference of two light beams which at a wavelength λ may be resolvedaccordi ng to the RAYLEIGH criterion in the focal plane (i.e. in the plane of the exit slit). The theoretical resolving power is always better than the actual one. Therefore, monochromators are sometimes characterized by the reciprocal of their linear dispersion, which is nothing else but the ratio of the spectral slit width in Å to the corresponding geometrical slit width in mm. The drawback of this criterion lies in the fact that nothing is said about the minimal slit width as mentioned above.

As dispersing elements, *prisms* or diffraction *gratings* are used. The resolving power of the prism depends on its size and material. Glass prisms of equal size have about three times the dispersive power of quartz prisms. Glass cannot, however, be used below 370 nm where it absorbs strongly. The resolving power of prisms decreases rapidly with increasing wavelength. For gratings, on the other hand, it is constant in the whole region and depends on the number of grooves and on the spectral order. For every unit increase of spectral order, the dispersion is doubled. However, the intensity of the spectrum decreases rapidly for higher orders so that spectra of the first or second order are generally used. Gratings usually have a blaze (i.e. given shape of grooves), so that the light is concentrated into a certain order and a certain wavelength region. To cover the whole wavelength region used, sometimes two interchangeable gratings are mounted in one instrument (176).

In recent years monochromators with diffraction gratings are be-coming more popular, mainly because the production of grating replicas has become less expensive.

If no monochromator is available, spectrographs may be adapted for atomic absorption work. Exit slits with attached photomultipliers are mounted instead of the photographic plate. More than one line may then be measured simultaneously (64). In general, spectrographs have a higher resolving power than monochromators.

4.3 LIGHT DETECTORS

In atomic absorption spectrophotometry, photoelectric detectors are used in general, although some research work has been also done with photographic plates. When the radiation flux measured is high enough, phototubes or photocells may sometimes be used. However, only *photomultipliers* have so far gained universal application.

A photomultiplier is a tube with a photosensitive electrode, (a photo-cathode) and several electrodes (known as dynodes). A high voltage is divided among them by a set of resistors. The total number of electrodes may be up to 13. The photocathode has the highest negative voltage and the voltage drop between each two successive electrodes is from 50 to 90 V. A photoelectron released by the cathode is attracted to the first dynode, gains kinetic energy and by its impact releases several new secondary electrons. These are attracted in their turn to the next dynode and release several more electrons each. The process continues until the last electrode, the anode, receives an avalanche of electrons. This multiplied photocurrent may be measured directly between the last dynode and the anode.

The resistors dividing the voltage must have such a value that the photocurrent through the tube is small compared with the current through the resistances or the potential difference between the plates will alter. Usually they have values from 100 to 500 kΩ.

The *spectral sensitivity* of a photomultiplier depends on the photo-sensitive coating of the cathode and the transmission of the tube en-velope. Most often alloys of alkali metals with antimony and silver or bismuth are used. They may be eventually activated with oxygen. The spectral sensitivities of the different alloys are shown in Fig. 4.2. With photomultipliers, radiation fluxes of $10^{-6} - 10^{-11}$ lumen may be

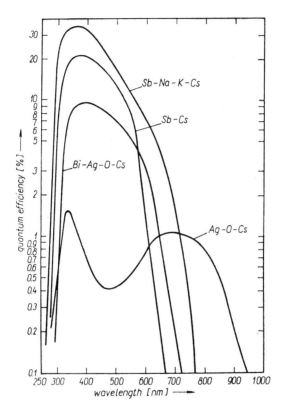

Fig. 4.2. Spectral sensitivity of different photocathode materials. The quantum efficiency of the photocathode is the ratio of number of emitted electrons to number of absorbed light quanta

measured. The sensitivity is usually between 10 and 100 A/lumen and the maximum current is about 10 μA. For higher outputs, the signal falls rapidly due to fatigue of the dynode surfaces.

An important property for estimating the quality of a photomultiplier is its *dark current*. This is the current flowing through the tube when the high voltage is applied, but no light is falling on the photocathode. This dark current is caused mainly by thermo-emission at the photocathode and emission caused by the electric field between the dynodes. Thermo-emission may be effectively reduced by cooling the multiplier with dry ice or liquid nitrogen. The fluctuations of the dark current known as the dark noise, is an important component of the detector noise. It increases considerably as the voltage applied increases. It is also proportional to the square root of the radiation energy falling on the photocathode. The noise is also increased if the voltage applied is not uniformly divided between the individual dynodes (the resistors must, therefore, be selected), and by any leaks in the insulation between the electrodes.

The gain of a multiplier depends exponentially on the applied voltage. The high tension power supply voltage must, therefore, be well stabilized, to at least 0·05%. In contrast to general use, the positive pole is earthed in this application.

CHAPTER 5

INSTRUMENTATION

5.1 THE DIRECT CURRENT MEASURING DEVICE

Two fundamentally different types of measuring systems must be distinguished, namely, instruments which measure *unmodulated* and *modulated signals*. In unmodulated systems the light from the source is falling continually on the photodetector producing a d.c. signal. All radiation from the flame at the wavelength measured is also falling on the detector, and influences the light intensities measured. Although the flame emission may be corrected for by subtracting off the indicator deflection observed with the light source shielded, additional errors are naturally introduced. The use of d.c. measuring devices is, therefore, limited to wavelength regions where common flames do not emit (i.e. only to the ultraviolet region).

The feasibility of using a d.c. measuring device depends also on the brightness of the light source. For instance, with vapour discharge lamps, even alkali metals having their lines in the visible region may be measured, because the flame emission is much smaller than that of the vapour discharge lamp.

The photocurrent of common photomultipliers is in the range 0·01–1 μA and may be measured directly with a galvanometer. Often devices for compensating for the zero deflection are added. These may be used simultaneously for scale expansion. A possible scheme is shown in Fig. 5.1.

Scale expansion is used when measuring very small absorption values. With a tenfold scale expansion transmission values between 90 and 100% are measured on the whole scale and the precision of the measurement is increased. The possibility of scale expansion is limited by fluctuations in other parts of the instrument (i.e. the photodetector, the flame and the light source).

A load resistance may be used instead of a galvanometer and the volt-age measured with an electronic (i.e. high input impedance) voltmeter. The load resistor must be a high quality with low thermal noise. Its value may be up to 100 MΩ.

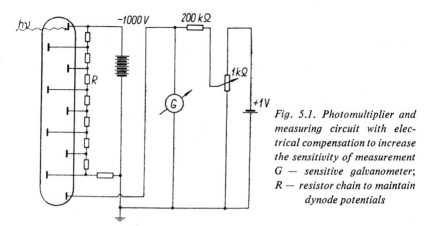

Fig. 5.1. Photomultiplier and measuring circuit with electrical compensation to increase the sensitivity of measurement G — sensitive galvanometer; R — resistor chain to maintain dynode potentials

The application of a d.c. measuring device is usually limited to the ultraviolet region. Its main advantage is simplicity and good performance. An important condition is that the circuit should be properly earthed.

5.2 THE MODULATED MEASURING SYSTEM

To eliminate unwanted radiation from the flame, the light source emission is modulated and only the alternating component of the photocurrent is amplified and measured. The direct current component caused by flame emission is thus eliminated. Instruments with signal modulation have a universal application. The electronic system is more complicated if good stability and high performance are required. A relatively simple scheme is described by Box and Walsh (54).

The voltage on a load resistance may be measured with a common a.c. voltmeter. However, the noise level is then relatively high because these voltmeters measure in a broad frequency pass band. The signal to noise ratio may be improved by using narrow pass band amplifiers tuned to the modulation frequency. The root-mean-square noise output of the amplifier is proportional to the square root of the pass band. Thus, the narrower the pass band, the better the signal to noise ratio. This ratio may be further improved by combining a frequency selective amplifier with a phase-sensitive detector. This combination, based on the principle of *synchronous detection*, brings best results (1, 195).

The modulation of the light beam may be performed either by mechanical choppers (rotating sectors or vibrating shields) or by supplying the hollow cathode lamps with pulsating current. So far, little is known about the optimum modulation frequency. It seems that the frequencies used in commercial instruments are chosen according to technical possibilities rather than because of other more fundamental reasons. The frequencies used are usually between 50 and 450 Hz. Higher frequencies have probably some preference because low-frequency components prevail in the flame noise.

5.3 DOUBLE-BEAM SPECTROPHOTOMETERS

Among the different types of spectrophotometers, double-beam and single-beam instruments may further be distinguished. The optical scheme of the Perkin-Elmer model 303 spectrophotometer is reproduced in Fig. 5.2 (176). The light beam from the light source falls on a rotating chopper provided with mirrors. Here it is divided in two. The reflected beam passes through the flame and recombines with the reference beam. Both fall on the monochromator slit and on the photodetector, and the corresponding signals are divided and compared in the electrical system. A deflection from a null-indicator results if the two signals are not equal. This deflection is then compensated for by adjusting a potentiometer across which a reference potential is applied. This potentiometer may than be calibrated with a scale in percentage absorption.

The advantages of a double-beam instrument in atomic absorption are a matter of discussion. In absorption spectrophotometry of solutions the reference beam passes through the solvent and eliminates its absorption. In atomic absorption the reference beam does not pass through the flame and the flame gases may absorb considerably in some wavelength. The advantage of the double-beam instrument, therefore, lies primarily in eliminating instabilities of the light source emission. However, nothing is noted about the light source contributions to the final fluctuations (197). RUSSELL, SHELTON and WALSH (295) did not find a better performance with double-beam instrument. This is in agreement with the findings of BODRECOVA et al. (49) that for good hollow cathode lamps

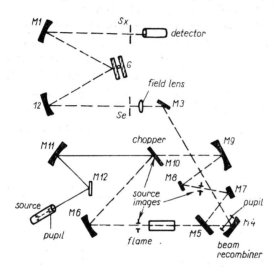

Fig. 5.2. Optical scheme of the Perkin-Elmer 303 double-beam spectrophotometer

the fluctuations of the signal emitted are below 0·1%. On the other hand, several authors achieved better precision in the determination of low concentrations by adapting their instruments to the double-beam principle. The precision improved by a factor or two (130) or three (160).

It is our impression that double-beam instruments have in general a better photometric precision. However, this is exploited only when the contribution of the flame noise, either by absorption of the measuring beam or by flame emission, is small.

From this point of view, better performance could be expected from measuring two different lines belonging to the same element with a small wavelength difference, the analytical line being absorbed and the reference line unabsorbed by free atoms in the flame. This method, suggested by MENZIES (235), has several advantages. All of the light source fluctuations, the background absorption fluctuations and the flame fluctuations, are eliminated. The major problem in applying this method is the choice of the two lines. So far ROBINSON has tried this method for iron (11). For other elements with less line-rich spectra the choice is very difficult, if not impossible.

5.4 OTHER MEASURING DEVICES

The most expensive part of the atomic absorption spectrophotometer is undoubtedly the monochromator. Therefore, several means for lowering the requirements on their performance or for eliminating optical mono-chromators altogether have been proposed.

If only those parts of the spectrum which carry information about the element determined are modulated, the requirements on the spectral pass band are lowered and less expensive monochromators with lower resolving power may be used. This principle is exploited with so-called *selective modulators* (53). These are high brightness hollow cathode lamps supplied with a direct current. The radiation passes through an additional hollow cathode (see Fig. 5.3) supplied with an alternating

Fig. 5.3. Selective modulator

current. Here, atomic vapour is generated with the frequency of the supply current and absorbs the resonance lines emitted. As a result only resonance lines are modulated by absorption. All other lines passing through the region remain unaffected. By amplifying the alternating current component only, the resonance lines are measured with greater accuracy. Selective modulators bring about considerable improvement when measuring nickel and cobalt with low dispersion instruments (see Fig. 5.4).

A different way to exploit this principle is to shift the flame periodic-ally in and out of the path of an unmodulated beam. Thus, all resonance lines are periodically absorbed, whereas the rest are unaffected, and by measuring the alternating component only, they may be isolated (201).

Periodic absorption may also be brought about by interrupting the atomizing air stream and thus also the sample uptake. This is evidently possible only with total consumption burners, because only these react sufficiently quickly (155).

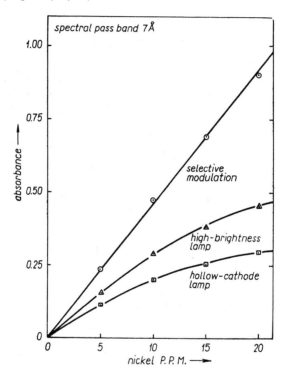

Fig. 5.4. Improvement of calibration curves using the selective modulation technique for the determination of nickel (53)
Spectral pass band 7 Å

Although the performance of such devices is, in general, worse than with good, standard equipment, the main advantage is the reduced requirements of the spectral pass band.

No optical monochromator at all is needed if a so-called *resonance monochromator* is used (328). This is again a hollow cathode lamp producing an atomic vapour of the element to be measured. Resonance radiation falling on this cloud of free atoms is absorbed and then re-emitted as fluorescent radiation in all directions (Fig. 5.5). If the incident beam is modulated, so is the fluorescent radiation, which is then measured by a photomultiplier placed in the side-arm of the resonance mono-chromator. By amplifying the modulated signal component only, the incident resonance radiation may be measured.

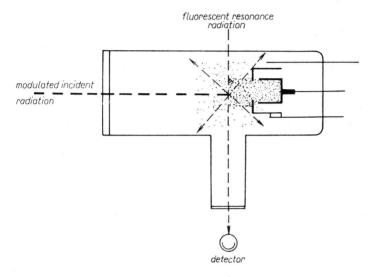

Fig. 5.5 Resonance detector

With resonance monochromators very cheap simple instruments, naturally with a limited application only, can be built.

5.5 REVIEW OF COMMERCIAL INSTRUMENTS

Commercial instruments for atomic absorption spectrophotometry are produced by several firms. New types appear at quite a high rate. As it is hard to judge the performance of the individual specimen without personal experience, we have tried to sum up all pertinent information in Table 5.1.

Table 5.1
REVIEW OF COMMERCIAL INSTRUMENTS

Firm	Model	Country	Type	Dispersing unit	Dispersion Å/mm	Burners and mixture used*	Type of light modulation used	Scale linear in
Techtron	AA4	Australia	single beam	grating	33	slot burner Ac—A;Ac—N; H—A; P—A	pulsating current 285 Hz	transmission
Techtron	AA100	Australia	single beam	grating	67	slot burner Ac—A;Ac—N; H—A; P—A	pulsating current 285 Hz	transmission
Hilger & Watts	Atom-spek	England	single beam	quartz prism		slot burner Ac—A;Ac—N; P—A	pulsating current 400 Hz	absorbance
Unicam	SP90	England	single beam	quartz prism		slot burner Ac—A; Ac—A; Ac—N; P—A	pulsating current	transmission
Southern Analytical	A 3000	England	single beam	grating	60	slot burner 12 cm Ac—A, Ac—N, H—A	pulsating current 400 Hz	absorbance
Evans Elec-troselenium	EEL 140	England	single beam	grating	66	Ac—A;Ac—N	pulsating current	transmission

Manufacturer	Model	Country	Beam	Monochromator	Slits	Burner / flame	Modulation	Readout
Perkin-Elmer	303	USA	double beam	grating	6·5-UV 13 Vis.	slot burner Ac—A;Ac—N; H—A; P—A	rotating chopper	transmission
Perkin-Elmer	290	USA	single beam	grating	16	slot burner Ac—A;Ac—N; H—A; P—A	pulsating current	absorbance
Jarrell-Ash	82500	USA	single beam	grating	16	HETCO burner slot burner Ac—A;Ac—N; H—A; P—A; Ac—O; H—O; H—N	rotating chopper	transmission
Jarrell-Ash	82600	USA	12 channel single beam	grating	16	ditto.	pulsating current	transmission
Beckman	979	USA	single beam	grating	16	Beckman burner Ac—O, H—O slot burner Ac—A	rotating chopper	transmission
Optica	Dens-atomic	Italy	single beam	grating		Ac—A 5 cm		absorbance

* A — air   Ac — acetylene   H — hydrogen   N — nitrous oxide   O — oxygen   P — propane

CHAPTER 6

SENSITIVITY, PRECISION
AND ACCURACY

6.1 SENSITIVITY

When speaking about sensitivity, *absolute and relative sensitivity* must be distinguished. Absolute sensitivity is a certain minimum determinable amount of the element, reported in weight units. Relative sensitivity is the minimum determinable concentration of the element in a given matrix. In atomic absorption, absolute sensitivities are usually only reported when using the graphite furnace or a hollow cathode absorption source. For these two devices the sensitivity depends, namely, on the weight of the element and, therefore, also on the weight of the sample in the absorption medium.

For absorption flame photometry, a relative sensitivity in an aqueous solution is generally reported. It is defined as that concentration of the solution which, sprayed into the flame causes a 1% *absorption*, i.e. a 0·0044 absorbance.

This sensitivity, as follows from eq. (1.16), depends on the atomic absorption coefficient, on the absorption path length, the atomization efficiency and the resulting concentration of free atoms in the flame gases. Let us make a rough estimate of the sensitivities attainable.

The value of the absorption coefficient for an ideally monochromatic line (the so-called peak absorption) may be evaluated from eq. (1.22a)

$$\varkappa(0) = \frac{\varkappa_L}{\pi\delta_v} = \frac{e^2 f}{mc\delta_v}. \qquad (6.1)$$

Inserting the following values $f = 1$, $\delta_\lambda = 0·003$ Å at $\lambda = 3,000$ Å $\left(\delta_v = c\delta_\lambda/\lambda^2\right)$ an approximate value of 10^{-12} cm^2 results. In absorption measurements with solutions using complexes with a molar extinction coefficient of $\mu = 10^4$, the corresponding absorption coefficient related to a single molecule is approximately $10^{-16} - 10^{-17}$ cm^2. From this point of view, atomic absorption is in a much better position to obtain higher sensitivity.

The concentration of free atoms in the flame depends on the atomization yield and on the degree of dissociation of the particular compound in the flame. In Chapter 2, the relation between the molar concentration in solution (C), and the number of atoms of the particular element in a unit volume for complete dissociation was assumed to be

$$n = 10^{14}C.$$

Using this value and a 10 cm long absorption path length, the maximum sensitivity should be about a $5 \cdot 10^{-6}$ molar solution, i.e. $0.01 - 0.1$ ppm concentration. The sensitivity characterizes primarily the properties of the element mentioned.

6.2 DETECTION LIMIT

With most instruments less than one per cent absorption may be measured with good precision. Using scale expansion the difference of the absorbed and unabsorbed signals may be amplified only so much, until it is lost in the fluctuations of the signal itself. To express this *lowest detectable concentration* the term detection limit is used (308). This is defined as the concentration causing a deflection equal to three times the standard deviation of the fluctuations of the unabsorbed signal, or twice the maximum noise level of the fluctuations. Assuming a normal distribution for the fluctuations, both definitions are almost identical, the latter which is advantageous from a practical point of view being an approximation of the former. The detection limit depends on the stability of the measurement. The difference between sensitivity and the detection limit primarily defines the performance of the instrument. This detection limit may be several times lower than the sensitivity.

Designating the photocurrent caused by the radiation flux J_0 (i.e. by spraying pure solvent) as I_0, and the photocurrent when spraying a solution with the detection limit concentration as I_{min}, this definition of detection limit may be expressed as

$$I_0 - I_{min} = 3\sigma_{I_0}. \tag{6.2}$$

Here σ_{I_0} is the standard deviation of the noise. From the BEER-LAMBERT Law it follows that

$$I_{min} = I_0 \exp\left(-\varkappa n_{min} l\right). \tag{6.3}$$

Inserting this equation into (6.2), expanding the exponential and taking only the first two terms into account, the following relation results

$$3\sigma_{I_0}/I_0 = 3\sigma_{rel.} = \varkappa n_{min} l. \tag{6.4}$$

Thus, it follows that the detection limit depends on the relative magnitude of the fluctuations.

The individual parts of the instrument contribute to the final fluctuations to different degrees. According to the rule of the sum of squares, the final fluctuation may be expressed as the sum of the squares of the fluctuations of the source σ_{source}, the detection and measuring system $\sigma_{det.}$, and the flame σ_{flame} (if all exhibit random noise fluctuations).

$$\sigma_{rel.} = (\sigma_{source}^2 + \sigma_{det.}^2 + \sigma_{flame}^2)^{\frac{1}{2}}.$$

All the standard deviations are expressed as relative values. For the lowest detection limits all must be kept at their smallest possible values.

The light source fluctuations not only depend on the stability of the power supply but also on the construction and the preparation of the lamp. It seems that for good hollow cathode lamps the fluctuations are below 0.1% (49). Moreover, these fluctuations may be almost completely eliminated by using a double beam instrument (176, 297).

The flame noise is mainly caused by two different processes. For short wavelengths the flame gases absorb radiation, the acetylene-air flame below 250 nm, the hydrogen-air flame below 220 nm. This absorption is higher for fuel rich than for oxidant rich flames (130). Because part of the light passes around the flame, the flame flickering causes variation of the signal measured even when only pure solvent is sprayed into the flame.

On the other hand, the flame also emits radiation and any component with the frequency measured increases the flame noise. This effect takes place primarily in the longer wavelength region, above 370 nm. So far very little is known about the flame noise. It seems to be higher for lower frequencies (below 100 Hz) and higher for turbulent flames than for laminar ones. With the use of multiple light beam passes, it increases strongly, thus limiting the enhancement attainable by this means. The flame noise depends also on the construction of the burner and the spray chamber (51, 176).

For the sake of simplicity let us consider the measuring device (including the photodetector) as a whole. With high performance instruments the transmission may be measured with a precision of $0\cdot1-0\cdot25\%$ (176, 312) but only when the radiation flux falling on the detector is sufficiently large. Otherwise the signal is lost in the detector noise (378) — see Chapter 4.

The radiation flux falling on the detector may be increased by using wider entrance and exit slits. However, if the band-width is increased too much, some parasite line may also be included. The continuous radiation increases as the square of the width. This is faster than the directly proportional increase in the spectral line radiation. All parasite radiation has unpleasant consequences (see Chapter 7, paragraph 7.6). The flame may also radiate in the pass band measured. Although this is eliminated by amplifying only the alternating component, the detector noise increases with the square root of the total radiation energy falling on the detector.

The interrelation of all these factors determines the optimum slit width for the particular determination (374, 379). It depends, therefore, not only on the dispersion of the monochromator but also on the radiation emitted by the light source. From this point of view high brightness lamps bring considerable improvement in the detection limits.

The detection limits reported for the Perkin-Elmer model 303 instrument are given in Table 8.1 on page 104. WINEFORDNER and VICKERS (378, 379) compared calculated and experimentally found detection limits for sodium and cadmium.

6.3 PHOTOMETRIC ERRORS

To attain the highest precision of measurement, the concentration of the element in the solution sprayed should be chosen so as to be in the range of lowest measurement error. In absorption measurements without scale expansion, the noise due to the electrometer most often acts as the limiting factor (380) and this may be assumed to be constant in the whole range. If the scale of the electrometer is linear in transmission values the photometric error may be derived by differentiating the absorbance expression,

$$\frac{\Delta C}{C} = \frac{\Delta A}{A} = \frac{0.4343}{T \log(1/T)} \Delta T. \qquad (6.5)$$

Here, C is the concentration of the element in the solution, A the absorbance, T the transmission. This dependence is plotted in fig. 6.1. It may be seen that the error value is almost constant in the interval between 40 and 80% absorption (0.23–0.7 absorbance) and has a minimum for 67% absorption. Beyond this interval the error grows rapidly. If some parasite radiation is simultaneously measured, the error begins to increase rapidly at lower absorption values, depending on the ratio of the absorbed to unabsorbed radiation flux (see Fig. 6.1).

Some recent instruments are provided with scales linear in absorbance values. In this case the error in measurement of the absorbance values is constant and the error of determination of concentrations decreases with increasing absorbance values (312).

In atomic absorption, high absorption values are seldom measured. To attain 40% absorption a fifty-fold increase in the concentration, above the sensitivity concentration is required. When determining trace elements this would require too high a concentration of salts in the solution sprayed. Besides, the error of smaller absorption measurements may be diminished by scale expansion which, for very low absorption value measurements, should always be used.

The photometric precision may be further increased by integrating the signal for a definite time interval (50) or by filtering out the short-time constant fluctuations. The use of a recorder is a great help, because the difference of the unabsorbed and absorbed signal may be read directly from the recorder tracing and may be corrected for any slow fluctuations of the zero absorption value (see Fig. 7.1). For such measurements the dependence in Fig. 6.1 does not hold good, because zero drift is already effectively assessed.

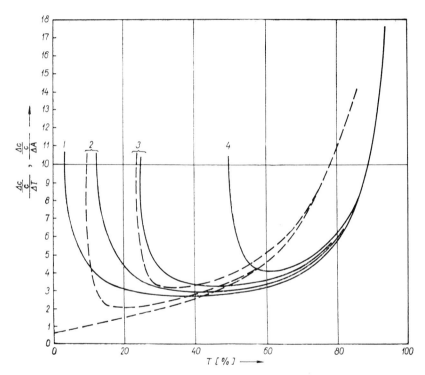

Fig. 6.1. Photometric errors at different transmission levels in presence of non-absorbed parasite radiation. P — the ratio of non-absorbed to absorbed radiation fluxes. (1) $P = 0$, (2) $P = 0.1$, (3) $P = 0.25$, (4) $P = 0.5$

Full line — the scale linear in transmission, interrupted line — the scale linear in absorbance

6.4 THE ASSESSMENT OF SPECIFIC ANALYTICAL PROCEDURES

For any new specific analytical procedure the precision and accuracy should be estimated. The precision is most often expressed as the standard deviation S calculated from repeated analyses. The appropriate formulas are

$$S = \sqrt{\left[\frac{\sum_i (x_i - \bar{x})^2}{n-1}\right]} = \sqrt{\left(\frac{\sum x_i^2 - n\bar{x}^2}{n-1}\right)},\qquad (6.6)$$

the latter being more convenient for numerical calculations. Here, x_i is the result of one measurement, $\bar{x}$ the arithmetic mean of all measurements and n the number of measurements. It is the experience of the authors that the major part of errors in atomic absorption results from setting the working conditions and drawing the working curve. It is, therefore, important that the repeated determinations be performed not in immediate succession but if possible on different days.

If duplicate analyses are performed the standard deviation of the results from the mean may be calculated from these analyses by using the formula

$$S = \sqrt{\left[\frac{\sum_i (x_i - x_i')^2}{M}\right]},\qquad (6.7)$$

where x_i and x_i' are two results of a duplicate analysis and M the total number of analyses. As mentioned in the preceding paragraph, the photometric error depends in the absorption value measured. The formula above may be used, therefore, only when the concentrations of all the samples used is approximately equal.

The standard deviation expressed as a relative percentage (this is often more convenient) is called the "coefficient of variation"

$$C = \frac{S}{\bar{x}} 100 .$$

Using the standard deviation, the concentration interval in which with a given probability (i.e. for a given confidence level), the result may lay, can be enumerated. The confidence levels usually used in chemical analysis are 95% and 99%. By multiplying the standard deviation by the appropriate coefficient from Table 6.1 and adding and subtracting the resulting value from the concentration found, the concentration interval in which the right value should be, is given. Because the standard deviation calculated from a limited number of repeated measurements is only an estimate approaching the right value with increasing number of measurements, the coefficients in Table 6.1 also depend on this number.

To test the accuracy of a specific analytical procedure is much more difficult than to estimate its precision. The best way is to analyse some standard reference material of well established and attested composition. Such materials are nowadays issued for many metals, alloys, technological material and even natural material. If no such standards are available, the results must be compared with those of other reliable well-tested reference methods. If this cannot be done, at least either the results from different sample weights or volumes should be compared, or any known quantity of the element added to the sample at the very beginning of the procedure should be quantitatively recovered and checked.

These last two criteria are necessary but not always sufficient conditions for the validity of the specific analytical procedure.

Table 6.1

COEFFICIENTS FOR CALCULATING CONFIDENCE LIMITS

Number of measurements n	Confidence level	
	95%	99%
2	12·71	63·66
3	4·30	9·92
4	3·18	5·84
5	2·78	4·60
6	2·57	4·03
7	2·45	3·71
8	2·37	3·50
9	2·31	3·36
10	2·26	3·25
25	2·06	2·80
∞	1·96	2·58

CHAPTER 7

EXPERIMENTAL TECHNIQUES

In the following chapter the basic principles of the analytical method and working techniques will be given. The information presented may be of use only to those who are, or will actually be working with atomic absorption spectrophotometry. Only the flame method will be dealt with.

7.1 INSTRUMENT OPERATION

The operation and handling of the different types of atomic absorption spectrophotometers depends partly on their construction. For commercially produced instruments, operation manuals with detailed instructions, are always delivered simultaneously. Here, only some general rules will be mentioned.

The instrument should be placed on a solid table with enough free space around it for placing the samples during measurement. The cylinders with compressed gases should be fastened on and supplied with adequate reducing valves. For air a small laboratory compressor is advantageous. Acetylene should be purified by passing through concentrated sulphuric acid.

An exhaust hood should be placed over the burner to keep the flame gases and the aerosols from polluting the laboratory atmosphere. Corrosion of the instruments is thus reduced, not to mention protecting the health of the workers.

When the instrument is installed and all the necessary electric connectors plugged in the appropriate sockets, a hollow cathode lamp is placed in the holder, switched on and the recommended current set.

The lamp position and the optical system are adjusted to make the light beam fall on the entrance slit of the monochromator. The wavelength of the monochromator is set on the resonance line of the particular element by adjusting it slowly until the indicator reading is at a maximum. The position of the hollow cathode is then once more adjusted to maximize the reading of this indicator.

The burner position is then adjusted to make the light beam run along its whole length above the burner slot. The optimum height of the burner will vary somewhat from one element to another. For elements forming oxides the sensitivity is highest when the light beam passes just above the inner reaction cone. In these cases it is better to set the correct height after lighting the flame by measuring the absorption of some standard solution.

After the instrument has been aligned, as described above, the operating conditions are set. With the flame burning, the sensitivity of the detection system is varied to make the indicator deflection 100% transmission (zero absorption) when spraying pure solvent, and zero transmission with a shutter placed between the light source and the flame.

The sensitivity of the detection system may be varied by changing either the slit width or the gain setting of the electrical part of the detector. In general, the broadest slit compatible with an admissible spectral pass band is used.

For lighting the flame certain rules must be kept. In general, the oxidant is turned on first and turned off last, whereas the fuel is turned on last and turned off first. For hydrogen-air or acetylene-nitrous oxide flames the reverse order is sometimes recommended. However, by combustion of acetylene without the oxidant, soot is formed, so that an exhaust hood is imperative. In any case, the instructions of the producer should be carefully kept to when lighting the flame.

After the flame is lit pure solvent should be sprayed into it. Most often this is distilled water or an organic solvent. In the latter case, the fuel flow must be reduced to obtain the right fuel to oxidant ratio. After some 10–15 min, when the instrument has warmed up, the 100% and zero values and the wavelength setting should be checked again. The instrument is then ready for measurement. The suction capillary is immersed in the solution to be measured and the transmission value is read on the indicator unit. If the stability of the reading is inadequate, a larger time constant may be used. The time of spraying a sample solution necessary for reaching a steady state, then increases.

During measurement several *faults* may occur. If too high a concentration of solutions of highly volatile solvents are used, the atomizer may get blocked by crystallized salts. In such cases the absorption is low and unsteady. The atomizer must then be cleaned. If the flame looks ragged or coloured even when only spraying distilled water, salt has crystallized in the burner slot. The burner should be cleaned.

To avoid such malfunctioning, pure solvent should be sprayed from time to time, or even between every two samples when working with relatively concentrated solutions. After finishing the measurement, the atomizer and burner should always be washed through by spraying with distilled water. Corrosion of the metallic parts is thus at least partly prevented.

7.2 PREPARATION OF STANDARD SOLUTIONS

The concentration interval of the element to be determined cannot be chosen deliberately, because the sensitivity of determination is fixed by the element analysed, the flame and other factors. It cannot be influenced by changing the gain as in emission flame photometry. The optimum concentration interval from the photometric precision point of view lies between 20 and 80% absorption. This, for linear working curves, corresponds to an about 20 to 150-fold increase in concentration above the sensitivity limit.

If minor or even trace elements are to be determined using a simple dissolving of the samples, such a high concentration would mean too high a concentration of the elements of the matrix in the solution sprayed. This would cause some unpleasant effects, such as clogging of the burner and sprayer, the aerosol particles not being completely evaporated, etc. This would unfavourably influence the precision of the measurement. Therefore, lower concentrations, corresponding to absorption below 20% are often measured. In general, a 3–80 % absorption (0·015–0·7 absorbance) is quite acceptable.

For trace element determinations the lower limit is naturally given by the detection limit. The analyst should be aware of the fact that for such low concentrations the precision is lower and that scale expansion is recommendable.

Standard solutions must be prepared unless a standard addition method (see p. 94) is used. The number of standards used depends on the shape of working curves. For linear working curves only four or five standards for one decimal order are sufficient. If the working curves are bent and high precision is required the number of standards should be increased.

Standard solutions should resemble the samples as far as possible. Only by this method can all the processes taking place in the flame itself and before be expected to be similar. The most commonly occurring interfering effects are the total salt content other than that measured and the concentration of organic compounds in the solution sprayed. If the total salt content exceeds some 0·1%, similar amounts of the same salts should also be added to the standard solutions. Otherwise the evaporation rate of the aerosol in the flame may be affected and a blocking effect may take place. The concentration level at which different salts begin to assert themselves, naturally depends on their vapour pressure, on the flame temperature and on the mean size of the aerosol particles. For total consumption burners and for low temperature flames (coal gas-air), this concentration level is generally lower.

The lowest standard solution should always contain all the salts added and a zero concentration of the element to be measured. If a buffer solution is also added to the samples, the possible impurity of the buffer solution is thus simultaneously corrected.

Standard solutions with a very low concentration are, in general, unstable, because adsorption of ions onto the flask walls may take place. If a pure solution of an element is used as a standard, it should always be freshly prepared from stock solutions. If the standard solutions also contain some other salt, the danger of adsorption is diminished. Before use, the flask with the standard solution in should be shaken, because pure solvent is usually condensed in the neck.

If only a few determinations are to be made from the sample solutions, they are best prepared in measuring flasks of 50 or 25 ml volume. For a single measurement much less is required. The necessary volume may be diminished well below 1 ml by different arrangements using recorders (198), but, in general, the precision of such measurements is likely to be worse.

7.3 EVALUATION

According to the BEER-LAMBERT law, the absorbance is proportional to the concentration of the analysed element. Some instruments are provided with scales reading the absorbance values directly. If the indicator deflection is proportional to the radiation flux falling on the photocathode, then the transmission of the light through the flame is measured. The absorbance is then calculated as the inverse function of the transmission

$$A = \log 1/T.$$

If the deflection when spraying pure solvent is set to 100 scale divisions, the absorbance may easily be read on a logarithmic ruler, where a scale of inverse values and a logarithmic scale are both given. The use of a set of logarithmic tables is both faster and more precise.

If the pure solvent deflection has any other value, the absorbance must be evaluated from the relation

$$A = \log I_0/I,$$

where I_0 and I are deflections corresponding to the pure solvent and the sample, respectively. The absorbance values are then used for the evaluation of sample concentrations.

The technique of measurement and method of evaluation should be designed according to the task. For routine measurements in an extended concentration interval without any special claims on the precision of determination, the simple working curve method may be used. The procedure is shortly described as follows. Firstly, the standards and then the samples are measured successively. After every three, five or even more samples a standard solution is measured, to measure how the working curve changes with time. If the changes are small, the number of standards measured between each batch of the samples may be reduced. The absorbance values are then calculated and the working curve plotted. Any changes of the working curve in time may be observed from the standard solution measured between the samples. If some considerable change takes place, a new working curve may be easily plotted, because it passes through the origin and the bending is usually unchanged. The precision of the results (expressed as a relative deviation) is usually between 2 and 5%.

For measuring a very low concentration approaching the sensitivity limit, scale expansion should be used. For values between 80 and 100% transmission the absorption values may be plotted directly against concentration, because the deviation from linearity of the working curves is only slight. When measuring very small absorption values, the 100 % transmission setting is of utmost importance. Better precision may be achieved by using a pen recorder. From the chart recording any variation of the zero absorption may be corrected for and the precision of the small absorption value readings increased. Such a recorder trace is shown in Fig. 7.1.

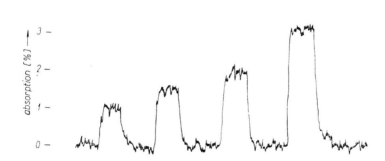

Fig. 7.1. Recorder tracing spraying 2, 3, 4 and 6 ppm of tellurium solutions, using a Perkin-Elmer, Model 303 spectrophotometer

If a measurement with high precision is required, the approximate content of the element in the sample should be known or a preliminary measurement made. If possible, the concentration of the element in the sample solution is then chosen to correspond to approximately 60% absorption. Two standard solutions with slightly higher and lower concentrations of the element to be determined are prepared. A scale expansion is used and the scale shifted to make the two standard solution readings lie at the two ends of the scale (199). That is, both the zero and 100% transmission deflections lie outside the scale. The sample and the standard solutions are then measured in order of increasing concentration and the measurement is repeated several times. The mean absorption values are then plotted and as for a sufficiently small concentration interval the curvature of the absorption-concentration dependence may be neglected, the unknown concentration may be inferred by linear interpolation. A recorder may again be used. For this kind of measurements the coefficient of variation (see p. 86) may even be below 1%.

The standard addition method

Sometimes the exact composition of the sample matrix is not known, the matrix is too complicated to imitate it with standard solutions, or only a small number of samples are to be analysed and the labour of

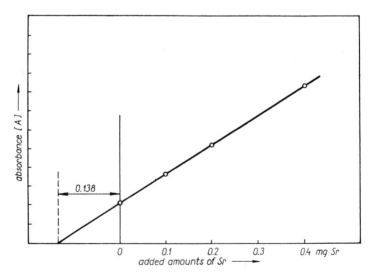

Fig. 7.2. Graphical evaluation using the standard addition method
The amount of strontium in the sample is 0·138 mgm

preparing complicated standard solutions would not pay. In these cases it is advantageous to use an addition method. It is somewhat more laborious but eliminates most of the interfering effects. The only condition for its application is that the working curves must pass through the zero absorbance point which is generally correct in atomic.

The concentration of the element determined must again be approximately known or estimated. Three separate equal fractions are pipetted from the sample solution and to two of them definite amounts of the element to be determined are added. If the amount of the element in the sample is x, suitable additions are x and $2x$. All three parts are then filled up with solvent to a definite volume and are then ready for measurement. The absorbance values are plotted against the added amount of the element and a line is drawn through the three points. It intersects the abscissa on the side of negative concentration values (see Fig. 7.2) and the point of intersection indicates the amount of the element present in the sample.

For a precise determination the working curves must be linear. If the working curves are curved, errors are introduced (200). If from previous measurements the linear working curves are guaranteed, a single addition is sufficient. The unknown amount then may be calculated from the equation

$$x = \frac{A_x z}{A_{x+z} - A_x},$$

where A_x and A_{x+z} are the absorbances of the solution without and with the additions respectively, z the amount added and x the amount sought. For small absorption values, i.e. below 10%, absorption values may be used instead of absorbance values.

7.4 THE CHOICE OF THE ANALYTICAL LINE

For most elements the analytical line generally used is the resonance line with the *greatest oscillator strength* corresponding to the transition from the ground state to some higher excited state. This line also secures the highest sensitivity, as follows from eq. (6.1) on p. 80. However, for some elements the choice may deviate from this because of any of the following reasons.

If the ground state is a multiplet with only slightly differing energies, the number of atoms occupying the levels with slightly higher energies but greater statistical weight may be higher than the number of atoms in the lowest energy level. From BOLTZMANN's equation (p. 26), it follows that for very low energies the exponential term approaches one and

$$n_k = n_i g_k / g_i \,.$$

This is, for instance, the case of aluminium. Its line at 3,082 Å, with an oscillator strength $f = 0.22$ corresponding to the transition from the ground state with a statistical weight of $g = 2$ has a lower sensitivity than the line at 3,093 Å line with an oscillator strength $f = 0.23$ corresponding to a transition from the level with an energy of some 0.13 eV above the ground state and a statistical weight of $g = 4$.

In some cases lines originating from metastable levels may also prove more sensitive if the spectrum emitted is very line-rich and some non-absorbing line is present in the spectral band-width isolated with the resonance line. These cases should, however, be less frequent with high brightness lamps. Sometimes, if the filler gas has been wrongly chosen, this parasite line may even belong to the inert gas present (see p. 48).

Another limiting factor may be due to the optical transmission or the flame gases. For elements with lines in the far ultraviolet region especially (e.g. Se, As, Hg), the most sensitive line may either be completely inaccessible (Hg 1850 Å). Alternatively, the noise caused by the necessity to exploit the full sensitivity of the photodetector or the contribution of the absorption of flame gases may be so high that a better detection limit may be achieved with a less sensitive line which lies in a region where the flame noise is lower (As 1937 Å).

Thus, for some elements the line giving optimum sensitivity may differ according to the working conditions used, i.e. the monochromator pass band, the light source, the flame, etc. In these cases which are, however, an exception rather than a rule it is best to find out for oneself which line brings best results under the conditions used. Many lines and some of their important properties are given in Table 9.13 at the end of the book.

7.5 INTERFERENCE EFFECTS AND THEIR ELIMINATION

For precise and accurate work in atomic absorption flame photometry, the analytical conditions must be chosen in the right way, so that no disturbing factors may influence the results and all interference effects must be eliminated or corrected.

Interference effects in absorption and emission flame photometry are a popular topic, but so far the terminology accepted by different authors is far from unanimous. To secure full comprehension of the following discussions a short outline of the classification adopted in this book will be given. All interference effects may be divided in two groups.

The first group, the so-called *spectral interferences*, are all attenuations of the radiation measured, caused by other effects than the particular atoms to be measured. This may entail light scattering by unevaporated salt particles, absorption by molecular bands or other continua, or even absorption by foreign atoms (if their line is emitted by the light source and lies in the pass band isolated by the monochromator). All the above will be dealt later in this chapter.

The second group comprises all interferences brought about by any *changes in the physical processes* taking part in flame photometry (see Fig. 7.3). These may be further divided into *transportation interference effects*, condensed phase interference effects, and interference effects in the *gaseous phase*. To the first of these (i.e. transportation interference effects), belong all factors affecting the amount of the sample entering the flame. The most important factors are viscosity (influencing the sample uptake), the surface tension (influencing the size of the aerosol droplets), and the vapour pressure of the solvent (influencing the evaporation rate and condensation losses). These were discussed more thoroughly in Chapter 2, paragraph 2.1. Transportation effects also occur with total consumption burners, because, for instance, the droplet size distribution may influence the number of droplets passing unevaporated through the flame. Because transportation effects affect all elements equally, they constitute interferences not specific to particular elements. These may be eliminated by using an internal standard. This principle was exploited in automatic analysers (63).

To the second of these interference effects belong *factors affecting the evaporation rate* of the solid particles in the flame. These may be both

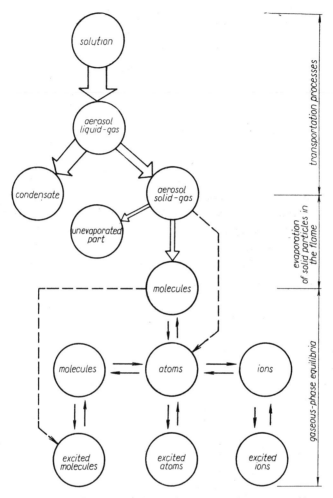

Fig. 7.3. Scheme of physical and chemical processes taking place in flame photometry

specific and non-specific. If the element to be determined (analyte) does not form any compounds with the interfering element (interferent), a non-specific blocking effect results. If, on the other hand, the analyte or some of its compounds undergo any sort of chemical reaction, or form a new phase with different thermochemical properties (e.g. formation of involatile compounds), the interference is specific (16A).

Blocking effects cause only relatively small depressive effects and for this the concentration of the interferent must, in most cases, be considerable. Simple blocking effects are usually corrected by adding the blocking element to the standard solutions. When some chemical reaction is involved the depressive effect, on the other hand, may be great even when the interferent is in comparable quantities to the analyte. The effect of aluminium and the phosphate anion on the measurement of the alkali earth metals is a well-known example (see Chapter 2, paragraph 2.2 and Chapter 9, paragraph 9.2). The possible ways to eliminate this interference are the dilution of the sample, the use of high temperature flames, measurement higher in the flame where the evaporation of the compounds is completed, or the use of releasing elements including some organic compounds.

Amongst *interference effects in the gaseous phase, dissociation* and *ionization equilibria* are the most important. The only way to eliminate this sort of interference is to stabilize the particular equilibria by adding appropriate *buffers* to the solution. They have been dealt with in Chapter 2, paragraph 2.3 and Chapter 9, paragraph 9.1.

When dealing with interferences the reader should bear in mind that the components causing interference may affect more than one of the discussed mechanisms. For instance, organic solvents affect both the transportation of the aerosol into the flame, and the vaporization and dissociation equilibria in the flame. This is one of the reasons why the so-called organic solvent effect is one of the most intriguing. The mechanism of the interference effect of one single compound may also differ according to the conditions used, such as flame temperature or whether a total consumption burner or a laminar flame is used.

Summing up, *three ways for eliminating interference effects* are used in general. Firstly, standards imitating the sample composition may be prepared. This method is reliable but laborious. It cannot be used if the overall composition of samples is not known or if it varies from sample to sample.

The second, most suitable method, from the analytical point of view is to add buffer solutions to both the standards and samples. The choice of the particular buffer naturally depends on the mechanism of the interference taking place. The various buffers most often used are discussed in the chapter dealing with analytical applications.

A third method for eliminating interference effects is the use of addition methods as described in paragraph 3 of this chapter.

7.6 UNABSORBED PARASITIC RADIATION

Any radiation present in the monochromator band-width not belonging to the measured line has an unfavourable influence. By increasing its share of the total radiation transmitted, the slope of the working curves and the sensitivity of determination diminish and the *working curves bend.* If the parasitic radiation belongs to some foreign line (a non-resonance line of the element measured, of the cathode material or of the filler gas) it may often be eliminated by using a narrower slit. The suitable slit width may best be determined by measuring the absorption change with increasing slit width. For narrow slit values the absorption is constant, but as soon as some other line appears in the pass band measured, a decrease of the absorption values begins. The highest slit width not causing an absorption decrease is best, because by increasing the slit width radiation flux increases correspondingly and therefore smaller gain setting may be used. This reduces the relative noise of the photo-detector.

If the parasitic radiation cannot be eliminated by choosing a narrower slit, the working curves may at least be straightened by setting the indicator deflection corresponding exclusively to this parasitic radiation on the scale to be zero (271). In practice, this is done as follows: A very strong solution of the analysed elements is sprayed and it is assumed that the resonance line is fully absorbed. The residual deflection belonging to the parasitic radiation is then set to the zero value.

If some resonance line of another element lies in the spectral pass band and is simultaneously emitted by the light source, then the presence of this element in the sample may influence the determination. However, this is a very rare case of spectral interference and may be completely eliminated by using a source emitting only the spectrum of the element to be determined (293).

If the parasitic radiation belongs to a continuous background emitted by the light source then choosing a narrower slit brings only an improvement. No complete elimination is possible. To straighten the working curves the deflection corresponding to the continuous measured on either side of the analytical line should be set to the scale zero.

Sometimes, when measuring wavelengths near the edges of the spectral sensitivity range of the optical detector, stray light may also influence the detector readings. In general, this happens only if d.c. measuring devices are used and the flame emits strongly (as in presence of high sodium or calcium contents in the solution sprayed). Because stray light has a completely different wavelength, it may be eliminated by using colour filters. The yellow sodium doublet may be eliminated by a neodymium filter.

7.7 BACKGROUND ABSORPTION

An important interference effect is the attenuation of the light beam caused by other mechanisms than atomic absorption. This effect is often called *non-selective absorption*, because it depends much less on the wavelength setting than true line absorption. Two different explanations have so far been presented. Either light scattering by unevaporated aerosol particles, or molecular absorption can be responsible. To decide which of these two mechanisms actually takes place, an estimation of the aerosol particles size is necessary. For very small particles with a diameter less than one-tenth of the wavelength of the radiation measured, light scattering according to the RAYLEIGH theory should take place, i.e. it should be proportional to the fourth power of the inverse value of the wavelength ($\sim \lambda^{-4}$). A steep increase for the shorter wavelengths may therefore be expected. WILLIS (364) actually found a similar wavelength dependence when spraying with 5% solutions of NaCl, K_2SO_4 and $CaCl_2$ in a low temperature flame. For larger particles, light scattering according to the MIE theory takes place and only a slight wavelength dependence should be expected.* GIDLEY (130) actually found such slight wavelength dependence when spraying with 10% solutions of Ti, Zr and Hf.

KOIRTYOHANN and FELDMAN (189) and KOIRTYOHANN and PICKETT (190) using absorption tubes, found distinct maxima and minima in continuous absorption spectra of alkali halides corresponding to the dissociation of gaseous alkali halides into free atoms. Similar results were also found directly in flames where molecular absorption spectra of CaOH and SrOH were observed (66, 191).

KOIRTYOHANN and PICKETT (192) estimated the size of the aerosol particles and calculated the light scattering according to the MIE theory. The scattering values found experimentally were several times higher. They concluded that non-selective absorption is caused primarily by other effects than light scattering.

So far there is not sufficient data on these effects. But it is evident that non-selective absorption is higher in low temperature flames than in hot flames (acetylene-air). According to the findings of BILLINGS (46) non-selective absorption may take place if the total salt content of the solution sprayed exceeds some 0·1%. However, the absorption values are relatively slight.

With absorption tubes where the absorption path length is considerably longer and the temperature lower, many compounds have a non-selective absorption effect. A very unpleasant one is the effect of sulphuric acid or the alkali halides.

Non-selective absorption may be corrected for by measuring the absorption of some non-resonant line in the neighbourhood of the analytical line and this absorbance is subtracted from the analytical line absorbance. Lines used for correction may belong to the element analysed, some other element present in the cathode material, or it may be a filler gas line. The wavelength difference of the two lines should naturally be as small as possible. If no such line is available the continuous spectrum of a hydrogen lamp may be used (190).

---

* Vide: MIE, *Ann. der. Physik,* **25**, 377 (1908).
  D. M. WOODWARD, *App. Optics,* **2**, 1205 (1963).

CHAPTER 8

ANALYTICAL POSSIBILITIES OF ATOMIC ABSORPTION FLAME SPECTROMETRY

In the former chapters the principles of atomic absorption spectroscopy, instrumentation and working techniques have been dealt with. However, most workers employed in analytical laboratories who are faced with the problem of whether to use atomic absorption for their particular analytical task are mainly interested in its analytical possibilities. Here, we shall try briefly to characterize this question.

In principle, concentrations of all elements can be determined but for some the method presents serious technical problems. The main factors limiting the applicability of atomic absorption flame spectrometry are the following:

(I) The main resonance lines of some elements lie in the vacuum ultraviolet region of the spectrum, where absorption by the atmosphere takes place. So far the line with the shortest wavelength measured is the selenium at 196 nm. In this region there is considerable absorption by the flame gases, so that the measurement is rather difficult. For such elements other means of absorption medium production should be tried (e.g. cathode sputtering or graphite tubes).

(II) Compound sof some elements formed in the flame are so stable that their evaporation and dissociation are negligible. The concentration of free atoms in the flame gases is, therefore, too low and the sensitivity poor. Although with the introduction of high temperature flames this group of elements has been considerably reduced, there are still some elements which evade measurement.

When considering the application of any method, the most important information is its sensitivity or the detection limit for the particular element. This data is given in Table 8.1 for acetylene-air and acetylene-

Table 8.1

SENSITIVITIES AND DETECTION LIMITS
REPORTED FOR THE PERKIN-ELMER MODEL 303 SPECTROPHOTOMETER

Element	Line $\mathring{A}$	Sensitivity ppm	Detection limit ppm	Oxidant
Ag	3,281	0·1	0·01	air
Al	3,093	1·9	0·1	N_2O
As	1,937	2	0·5	air
Au	2,428	0·5	0·1	air
B	2,498	35	6	N_2O
Ba	5,536	0·4	0·1	N_2O
Be	2,349	0·03	0·003	N_2O
Bi	2,231	0·8	0·2	air
Ca	4,227	0·1	0·01	air
Cd	2,288	0·03	0·01	air
Co	2,407	0·2	0·05	air
Cr	3,579	0·15	0·01	air
Cs	8,521	0·5	0·05	air
Cu	3,247	0·15	0·01	air
Fe	2,483	0·15	0·02	air
Ga	2,874	2·5	0·1	air
Ge	2,652	2·5	1	N_2O
Hf	3,072	15	15	N_2O
Hg	2,537	15	0·5	air
In	3,040	0·9	0·05	air
Ir	2,850	35	4	air
K	7,665	0·1	0·005	air
Li	6,708	0·07	0·005	air
Mg	2,852	0·01	0·003	air
Mn	2,798	0·1	0·005	air
Mo	3,133	0·4	0·05	N_2O
Na	5,890	0·04	0·005	air
Nb	3,349	40	20	N_2O
Ni	2,320	0·2	0·03	air
Pb	2,170	0·5	0·03	air
Pt	2,659	2·7	0·2	air
Rb	7,800	0·2	0·005	air
Re	3,460	20	1	N_2O
Rh	3,435	1	0·03	air

Table 8.1 continued

Element	Line $\overset{\circ}{A}$	Sensitivity ppm	Detection limit ppm	Oxidant
Ru	3,499	2	0·3	air
Sb	2,176	1	0·2	air
Sc	3,912	0·5	0·2	N_2O
Se	1,961	2	1	air
Si	2,516	1·2	0·1	N_2O
Sn	2,246	2	0·8	air
Sr	4,607	0·2	0·02	air
Ta	2,714	30	6	N_2O
Te	2,143	2	0·1	air
Ti	3,643	2	0·2	N_2O
Tl	2,768	0·8	0·2	air
U	3,515	200	30	N_2O
V	3,183	1·2	0·1	N_2O
W	4,009	25	3	N_2O
Y	4,102	1·5	0·3	N_2O
Zn	2,138	0·04	0·005	air
Zr	3,601	15	5	N_2O

nitrous oxide flames. These figures correspond to the actual situation and there is no doubt that with further improvements in the instrumentation they will be improved in the future.

The sensitivity of any determination depends on the atomization yield, on the dissociation of the element in the flame, on the oscillator strength of the analytical line and on the spectrum of the light source. Next to these factors, the detection limit also depends on the photometric noise. The values reported may, therefore, vary for different instruments.

Although atomic absorption spectrometry is a relatively modern method, it has found ample use in many fields of human activities. So far most applications have been in the analysis of biological materials, i.e. in clinical, biochemical and agrochemical analyses (364). The samples are often fluid, so that they may be analysed directly after appropriate dilution. Mineralization, which is usually an unpleasant operation, is thus obviated.

Atomic absorption has also found great use in metallurgy (104). Although it cannot compete with optical and X-ray spectrometers as regards speed and cost per determination, the capital investment for the equipment required is incomparably smaller. If the number of analyses per day is not too high and the materials analysed varying, atomic absorption may prove preferable, because the standards may be easily prepared from aqueous solutions of pure reagents, whereas for optical and X-ray spectrometry, expensive metallic standards are required.

Another field for application is the chemical and petrochemical industry for the analysis of raw materials and the final products. Applications in geology and mining are also steadily increasing.

In all these fields the main advantages of atomic absorption flame photometry, i.e. its simplicity, speed, reliability and cheapness of equipment, are appreciated. Because of its specificity and sensitivity, direct determinations without chemical separation are possible in most cases. The only operation required is the dissolving of the sample which, after a possible addition of some buffer solution, is ready for measurement.

Although a comparison of analytical methods requires rough generalizations, we have tried to compare atomic absorption spectrometry with some common analytical methods as regards several aspects (see Table 8.2). In definite cases (i.e. for a particular element and a particular material), the result of the comparison may be completely the opposite. This may also be the case if special modifications of methods (e.g. inversive polarography) are compared.

The number of elements which may be determined by any particular method, as well as some of the less common methods of analysis, (e. g. activation analysis and mass spectrometry), which in some respects may be considered superior, is not reported in the Table.

From the methodological point of view, flame photometry is the most closely related method and comparison with atomic absorption is obvious. The absorption method attains higher sensitivity for elements with higher excitation energy. The flame temperature, which is often insufficient for excitation, secures complete dissociation of many elements, especially from the first and second subgroup of the periodic table. These elements may then be determined with a sensitivity comparable to the sensitivity of the alkali metals by emission flame photometry.

Table 8.2

COMPARISON OF ATOMIC ABSORPTION FLAME PHOTOMETRY
WITH OTHER ANALYTICAL METHODS

Method	*Sensitivity*	*Precision*	*Reliability and inter-ference effects*	*Speed and simplicity*	*Invest-ment costs*
Polarography	+	+	+	+	−
Colorimetry	−	0	+	+	−
Emission flame spectrophotometry	0	+	+	0	0
Emission spectro-graphy and spectro-metry	−	+	+	−	+
X-ray spectrometry	+	0	0	−	+

+ atomic absorption superior
− atomic absorption inferior
0 both methods approximately equal

One of the major advantages of all methods based on the measurement of line spectra is their high specificity. The signal, bearing information on the amount of the element present, is concentrated on a very narrow interval of wavelengths. However, full exploitation of this inherent specificity in emission poses great requirements on the performance of the optical instruments, so that sometimes high dispersion spectro-graphs are needed. In atomic absorption an equal specificity may be reached with cheaper low-dispersion instruments, because the wave-length interval measured depends primarily on the width of the spectral line emitted by the light source. Spectral interferences, so often a limiting factor in emission flame spectrophotometry, are almost unknown in absorption.

In the following chapter a review of analytical applications is given. The elements determined are divided into several groups according to their behaviour from the point of view of atomic absorption. For every group, general information on their common features, i.e. behaviour in the flame, their spectra, the possible interfering effects, etc., is discussed.

Afterwards every element is dealt with separately. A table of references on the applications published is attached to every group. These tables are arranged according to the materials analysed. Papers dealing with the analyses of particular materials for a number of elements with more emphasis on the material's problems are arranged separately in Table 9.10 on p. 148. Readers especially interested in the analysis of a particular material should firstly take a look at this Table.

CHAPTER 9

APPLICATIONS

9.1 THE DETERMINATION OF ALKALI METALS

The determination of alkali metals by absorption flame photometry is sensitive and precise, with relatively few interference effects. All the radiation interferences taking place in emission flame photometry are almost completely eliminated. On the other hand, absorption flame photometry is somewhat less sensitive than its emission counterpart. This is usually irrelevant, because in most cases the sensitivity is more than sufficient, at least for sodium, potassium and lithium. The absorption method has also a somewhat greater precision of determination.

The main resonance lines are in the visible or near infrared region. All are doublets, the component with the shorter wavelength having twice as high an intensity as the longer wavelength component. Their wavelength difference increases with atomic number. For lithium the doublet is usually unresolved.

All soluble alkali metal salts have relatively low boiling points so that all evaporate immediately after passing through the reaction zone. In the flame gases different processes take place (see Chapter 2). For alkali metals the most important are the dissociation and ionization equilibria. The formation of hydroxides is, with the exception of lithium and sometimes caesium, negligible (see Table 9.1). The dissociation constants of the alkali halides are given in Table 9.2, the ionization constants in Table 9.3. For these values the degree of ionization may be estimated for the particular experimental conditions. In the cooler coal gas-air flame, the ionization of alkali metals is small and dissociation plays a major role. In the hotter acetylene-air flame the dissociation of alkali halides is almost complete and the ionization equilibrium determines the concentration of free atoms present and hence the signal measured. It is well-known that by increasing the anion concentration in the solution sprayed (e.g. by adding free acids) a decrease in the

Table 9.1

DISSOCIATION DEGREE OF ALKALI METAL HYDROXIDES
IN AN ACETYLENE-AIR FLAME (158)

	%
Li	20
Na	100
K	70
Rb	80
Cs	45

Table 9.2

DISSOCIATION CONSTANTS OF ALKALI CHLORIDES
IN ACETYLENE-AIR AND COAL GAS-AIR FLAMES

	Acetylene K_{dis} *(atm)*	*Coal gas* K_{dis} *(atm)*
NaCl	$2 \cdot 2 \times 10^{-4}$	$6 \cdot 3 \times 10^{-6}$
KCl	$7 \cdot 9 \times 10^{-5}$	$2 \cdot 5 \times 10^{-6}$
RbCl	$4 \cdot 7 \times 10^{-5}$	$6 \cdot 3 \times 10^{-6}$
CsCl	$2 \cdot 6 \times 10^{-5}$	

alkali metal signal is observed. The mechanisms in the coal gas and acetylene flames differ. In the former, the decrease is caused by a shift in the dissociation equilibrium, whereas in the acetylene-air flame the dissociation is complete, and the decrease is caused by a shift in the ionization equilibrium. The electro-negativity of the anion atoms shifts the ionization reaction in favour of the ionized atoms. According to

Table 9.3

	Acetylene		*Coal gas*	
	K_{ion} *(atm)*	*Ionization degree %*	K_{ion} *(atm)*	*Ionization degree %*
Li	1.48×10^{-9}	5	9.28×10^{-13}	<1
Na	4.80×10^{-9}	15	4.16×10^{-12}	<1
K	1.80×10^{-7}	50	4.68×10^{-10}	7
Rb	3.90×10^{-7}	63	1.18×10^{-9}	11
Cs	1.45×10^{-6}	82	6.30×10^{-9}	23

ZHITKEWICH (394), free electrons are bound by the reaction

$$e + X \rightleftharpoons X^- ,$$

where X is a halogen atom. This reaction mechanism is confirmed by the decrease of line intensities of alkali metal ions found after the addition of halogens to the flame gases, and by the decrease of the free electron concentration in the flame gases as measured by a microwave technique (395). Other anions have similar effects, the only exception being the nitrate anion which is without influence. The reason for this is that the compounds resulting from its decomposition are present in excess in the flame gases already.

The effect of acids is more pronounced for direct sprayer burners because the volume of the solution introduced is many times higher than that of burners with cloud chambers. The errors caused by this effect seldom exceed 10%. Their elimination is relatively simple, because the concentration of anions in the solutions sprayed may easily be kept constant or the acids may be added in excess.

Much greater errors may be caused by ionization equilibria. With increasing concentration of an element in the analysed solution the ionization degree decreases, so that the concentration of atoms in the flame gases increases more rapidly than the concentration of the element in the solution and a bending of the working curves away from the concentration axis results. The addition of other alkali metals has a similar influence, the total concentration of free electrons in the flame gases increases, shifting the equilibrium in favour of neutral atoms. This is easily observed for elements with low ionization energies, i.e. caesium, rubidium and potassium. The mutual interference effect of alkali metals is a well-known phenomenon already dealt with by many authors (119, 266, 288).

For the elimination of the ionization interference effects, the addition of some easily ionizable element in such amounts so as to make the portion of electrons resulting from the interfering elements negligible compared with the portion of electrons resulting from this "buffering" element. Because the concentration of free electrons in the flame gases is given by the equation

$$P_e = \sqrt{(P_{M_1}K_1 + P_{M_2}K_2 + P_{M_3}K_3 + \ldots)},$$

where M_1, M_2, M_3 are the several alkali metals undergoing ionization, it is evident that the bigger the ionization constant of the buffer the smaller the added amount of the buffering element which need be used. Caesium (as the element with the biggest ionization constant) is therefore recommended. Because caesium salts are relatively expensive, potassium salts are more often used.

For alkali metals, with the exception of lithium, vapour discharge lamps are generally used as light sources. Because of their high emissive power, simple instruments with filters may be used as monochromators and barrier cell photodetectors may be used for measurement. The vapour discharge lamps should be supplied with the lowest current compatible with a stable operation of the lamp (0·3–0·5 amp). The discharge temperature is then lower, hence the emitted lines are narrower which means the working curves have a greater slope and are less curved.

All alkali metal resonance lines have very low excitation energies. Their spectral emission even from low temperature flames is considerable. With hollow cathode lamps a modulated system must invariably be used. When employing vapour discharge lamps, the radiation from the flame is often negligible compared with the radiation from the discharge lamp, and a d.c. measuring system may be used, though only in a limited concentration interval. Table 9.4 reviews all the papers dealing with alkali metal measurements.

Table 9.4

REVIEW OF PAPERS DEALING WITH ALKALI METALS

Elements determined						Material analysed	Reference
mentioned in the chapter				other elements			
Li	Na	K	Rb	Mg	Ca		
	Na	K				blood serum	361
	Na	K				blood serum	149
		K				oil field brines	48
			Rb			plants, soils	332
Li						plants, water	262
Li						sea water	30
			Rb			sea water, rocks	238
	Na	K		Mg	Ca	soils	84
	Na					pure limestones	287
Li						rocks, salt solutions	391
	Na					halophosphate phosphors	264
	Na	K				study	220
	Na	K		Mg	Ca	study	92
	Na					study	279
			Rb			study	310
	Na	K				study	216
Li						isotopic analysis	137
Li						isotopic analysis	217
Li						isotopic analysis	385
Li						isotopic analysis	386

Lithium

So far relatively few papers have been dedicated to the measurement of lithium concentrations by atomic absorption. The absorption method is less sensitive than the emission method for this element. On the other hand, it is free from spectral interferences by strontium and calcium molecular spectra which often make the determination of lithium by emission flame photometry impossible (391). Lithium has been measured in rocks, sea water and plants. The sensitivity using the line at 670·8 nm is about 0·07 ppm.

For lithium, hollow cathode lamps are always used. Because of its high volatility, their lifetime is relatively short. An alloy of lithium and bismuth has been recommended for the preparation of hollow cathodes. For laboratory made lamps, a graphite electrode supporting lithium metal has been found better than using supporting electrodes of magnesium, aluminium or brass (391).

Atomic absorption spectroscopy may be used for the determination of the isotopic composition of lithium. The isotope shift* for the Li^6 and Li^7 isotopes (0·16 Å) is several times greater than the width of the lines emitted by the hollow cathode lamp. No instrument with high

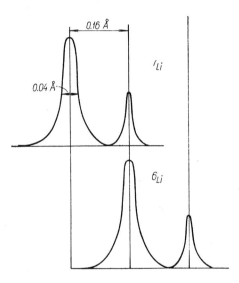

Fig. 9.1. Isotopic shift of the lithium doublet at 6,710 Å

resolving power is needed, but hollow cathode lamps with pure Li^6 and Li^7 isotopes only or lamps with enriched isotopes are necessary. The measurement is somewhat complicated by the fact that the isotope shift is comparable with the fine structure of the lithium spectrum, so that the stronger component of the Li^6 doublet coincides with the weaker Li^7 component (see Fig. 9.1).

---

* KUHN, H. G., *Atomic Spectra*, Longmans Green, 2nd Edn. (1969).

For an isotopic analysis the total lithium concentration must be known and eventually set to a definite value. For a given lithium content the absorbance measured with a pure Li^6 or Li^7 lamp (385), or the ratio of the two absorbances (137) against the relative Li^6 content is then plotted. Natural lithium contains about 7·5% of Li^6, but in different salts smaller contents have been found (137, 217).

A flame has also been tried as a light source instead of the hollow cathode lamps (217). Its disadvantage is its greater line width. GOLEB and YOKOYAMA (137) have used hollow cathode tubes as absorbing media.

Sodium

Sodium contents are often determined by atomic absorption. The sensitivity of the resonance doublet at 590 nm is 0·05 ppm. For the measurement of high amounts of sodium the doublet at 330 nm may be used (361), in which case the sensitivity is about a hundred times lower.

For sodium, hollow cathode (279, 361) or vapour discharge lamps are used, the latter according to some authors (220) securing a better signal to noise ratio.

Because of the smaller spectral interferences of the alkaline earth molecular spectra sodium may be determined in limestones in the ppm concentration level without difficulties. No background corrections are necessary (287). This is a great advantage when determining sodium traces. An addition method may easily be used, because the working curves run through the origin. With the emission method a background correction may be necessary and this might introduce additional errors.

Using sodium, dissociation and ionization interference effects readily take place. The concentration of cations and anions must, therefore, be kept constant. High salt contents in the samples should also be present in the standard solutions. When analysing limestones (287) and cement (335) calcium has to be added to the standards. This is especially important when using low temperature flames where the blocking effect readily takes place. In an acetylene-air flame no blocking effect of calcium on sodium has been observed (287). On the other hand, the ionization effect must be balanced out in this flame by potassium addition.

Usually, because of the high content of sodium in the samples, they may simply be diluted. Sodium has been extracted from fats with water. Solid samples must be dissolved and silicate materials are decomposed by hydrofluoric and sulphuric, or perchloric acids (44, 340).

Potassium

The determination of potassium by atomic absorption is equally easy. The main advantage, compared with the emission method, is higher precision. Vapour discharge lamps are usually used. Although the resulting sensitivity is lower than that with hollow cathode lamps, the signal to noise ratio is better and the detection limit for both light sources is about the same (220). If no potassium lamp is available, a sodium vapour discharge lamp may often be used, because it contains sufficient potassium as an impurity (4). Red sensitive photomultipliers are necessary because the potassium doublet is at 767 nm.

Ionization interference has been observed when analysing blood serum, containing some 300 ppm Na. WILLIS (361), therefore, suggests stabilizing the ionization equilibrium by adding 1,000 ppm sodium to both the samples and the standards. The influence of acids and other cations on potassium is similar to that of sodium.

Rubidium

The determination of rubidium concentrations by atomic absorption is less sensitive than by emission flame photometry. However, its great advantage is high specificity of determination. In emission flame photometry strong spectral interference of the potassium doublet hinders the use of the more sensitive component Rb 780 nm so that the less sensitive Rb 495 nm component must be measured. Unless a monochromator with high resolution is used for the emission method, the spectral interference of potassium causes a high background and a pen recorder for correcting this should be used. All these difficulties can be avoided with the absorption method. The more intense component at 780 nm is always measured without spectral interference of potassium taking place.

Because the sensitivity of the photomultipliers falls off steeply in the near infra red region, all scattered light of shorter wavelength increases the detector noise considerably. It is, therefore, recommended to filter out this radiation using a suitable filter (e.g. Jena R G 8), placed before the entrance slit (310).

To lower the degree of ionization of rubidium, either low temperature flames are used or the temperature of the acetylene-air flame may be lowered by the addition of nitrogen or carbon dioxide (332). The sensitivity is thus increased. A similar effect may be achieved by adding an excess of potassium. The influence of a varying content of the other alkali metals, especially potassium and caesium, must be eliminated by adding potassium to both the samples and the standards. For silicate rocks a minimum level of 3 mg of K ml. is recommended (290). Rubidium was measured in silicate rocks and minerals (44), in seawater (238), in soils and in plants (332).

Caesium

The problems of measurements of caesium contents are similar to those of rubidium. Vapour discharge lamps or electrode-less discharge tubes are used as light sources. The line at 852 nm exhibits a sensitivity of 0·15-0·5 ppm. The danger of ionization interference is even greater than for rubidium. No actual application has so far been published (147). Owing to the fact that the spectral sensitivity of the photomultipliers decreases rapidly towards the infra red region, attention must be drawn to the sensitivity of the detection system.

9.2 THE DETERMINATION OF ALKALI EARTH METALS

In this group we shall deal with magnesium, calcium, strontium and barium. Atomic absorption is often used for these. The greatest advantage is its specificity of determination, so that mixtures of two or more of these elements which are a problem in emission flame photometry, may easily be analysed. From the point of view of atomic absorption, magnesium differs somewhat from the rest; its determination is one of the most sensitive; much higher than the sensitivity of the others. Magnesium has its main resonance line in the ultraviolet region, the others in the visible region so that modulated light sources must be used with acetylene-air flames.

All these elements form oxides in the flame and also to a much smaller extent such radicals as MOH, MOH^+, etc. For complete dissociation high temperatures are essential. In an acetylene-air flame the following dissociation degrees have been reported: Mg 1·5%, Ca 4·7%, Sr 11%, Ba 0·21% (158). Any change in the composition of the flame gases may shift the dissociation equilibria and hence influence the concentration of the free alkali earth atoms in the flame.

If several cations and anions are present in the solution sprayed, involatile compounds with the alkali earth metals are formed, the evaporation of solid particles and the concentration of free atoms in the flame is decreased. This depressive effect has been reported for Al, Ti, Fe, Hf, Zr, Th, Cr, V, U, as well as for silicate, phosphate, sulphate and some other anions. This is well-known phenomenon in emission flame photometry and its mechanism has been discussed in several papers (96). The depressive effect may be observed only if both the alkali earth element and the interferent are present in the same solution. If the analyte and interferent are sprayed separately no such effect is observed (15). This confirms that the formation of the involatile compound proceeds during the evaporation and crystallization of the droplets and not in the gaseous phase. For magnesium and aluminium the formation of the spinel $MgAlO_4$ was confirmed by X-ray diffraction analysis of the aerosol as it left the flame (294).

From the analytical point of view the most important question arises as to how this depressive effect can be eliminated. If the concentration of the interferent is known and the sensitivity is sufficient, model standard solutions may be applied. The standard addition method may be used only if the interferent is in excess. Otherwise as the analyte concentration increases, the relative value of the depression decreases and the working curves are not linear. Their slope grows with increasing addition of the analyte.

The best elimination may be achieved by adding some releasing element (96) or organic compound to the solution. As releasing elements lanthanum, strontium or calcium have usually been used, although some other elements are also effective. The mechanism of the releasing effect is similar to the interference effect. The releasing element forms involatile compounds preferentially with the interferent, so that the analyte stays free (294). For complete release, the releasing element must be in considerable excess. Up to 2% lanthanum solution is sometimes recommended (340).

Another possibility is the use of organic compounds. For instance, oxine or ethylene diamine tetra-acetic acid (EDTA). According to some authors, the chelating properties of these compounds prevent the formation of involatile compounds by forming chelates either with the analyte or the interferent. Because the formation of chelates in strongly acid media is improbable, another hypothesis has been proposed which assumes the combustion of the organic compound and explosive disintegration of the aerosol particles and more complete evaporation (31). Because the formation of an involatile compound often requires the presence of the analyte and interferent in an oxidized form it seems probable that the organic compounds act through the reducing properties of carbon in the particles (294).

In the presence of organic compounds alone, the elimination of the depressive effect is not complete (349). However, combining the organic compounds with a releasing element, the elimination is more effective and the amount of the releasing element needed is considerably lower. Thus, in a 1% oxine solution 2,000 ppm lanthanum eliminate the depressive effect of 300 ppm aluminium (294). Similar results were obtained with lanthanum and EDTA (12, 272).

The possibility of using lower concentrations of the releasing element brings two advantages. The danger of clogging the burner by crystallized salts is diminished and the requirements on the purity of the releasing element salt used are less severe.

These interferences in the condensed phase depend considerably on the mean particle size of the aerosol and on the flame temperature. In a nitrous oxide-acetylene flame no interferences of this sort have been observed so far (27, 251). In low temperature flames, on the other hand, they are much more severe (114, 174).

Table 9.5
REVIEW OF PAPERS DEALING WITH ALKALI EARTH METALS

Elements determined		Material analysed	Reference
mentioned in the chapter	other elements		
Mg	Zn	brain tissue	73
Mg		serum	358
Mg		serum	360
Mg		serum	152
Mg		serum, urine	318
Mg		blood plasma	165
Mg Ca		serum	330
Ca		serum	392
Ca		serum	359
Mg		biological materials	91
Mg Ca		urine	362
Ca		saliva	252
Mg		plants	382
Mg	Cu Zn Fe	plants	81
Mg	Zn	chloroplasts	157
Ca		plants	82
Ca		plants	159
Mg Ca		plants	42
Mg Ca	Zn	animal nutrition	259
Sr		biological material, soils	87
Mg Ca	Na K	soils	84
Sr		oil field brines	47
Mg		coal	337
Sr		coal ash	34
Mg		limestones, cement	205
Mg		silicate rocks	251
Ca Sr Ba		glass	12
Mg	Cr Mn	Ni-alloys	29
Mg	Cr Mn	Ni-alloys	99
Mg		Al-alloys	206
Mg		iron	33
Mg		uranium	164
Mg		study	17
Mg		study	145
Mg		study	331

Table 9.5 continued

Elements determined		Material analysed	Reference
mentioned in the chapter	other elements		
Mg	Cu Ag Zn Au Pd Pt Rh	study	235
Mg	Cu Zn Cd Co Ni	study	120
Mg Ca		study	272
Mg Ca	Na K	study	92
Mg Ca Sr		study	294
Ca		study	95
Ca Ba		study	313A
Sr	Mo	study	83
Ba		study	66

The ionization interferences are much smaller than those for the alkali metals. In an acetylene-air flame ionization may take place for strontium and barium, but for calcium it is usually negligible. However, in the nitrous oxide-acetylene flame the degree of ionization is considerable and must be suppressed by the addition of some alkali metals.

Because of the complicated reaction equilibria in the acetylene-air flame, the gas flows of both the oxidant and the fuel must be meticulously watched during the measurement, because even minute changes influence the free atom concentration considerably. The height of the light beam above the burner must also be carefully set, because the flame profiles of the alkali earth elements display a relatively sharp maximum due to the formation of oxides (276, 294). Table 9.5 gives a review of papers dealing with this group of elements.

Magnesium

For the determination of magnesium, atomic absorption is most often used because it is undoubtedly the best of all possible methods for determining trace amounts of magnesium. The applications are very frequent in biology. Magnesium is one of the main biogene elements and its determination by other methods is complicated by the presence of calcium.

The resonance line Mg 285·2 nm lies in the most favourable wavelength region, where the flame neither emits nor absorbs. The sensitivity of 0·01 ppm is sufficient for a direct determination in most materials.

Hollow cathode lamps are generally used. The cathodes are usually machined from pure magnesium metal. If some magnesium alloys are used instead, the current needed for a sufficient emission of the magnesium line is much higher (~40 mA). Laboratory manufacture of hollow cathode lamps is easy, because magnesium sputtered from the cathode acts as a "getter" and keeps the filler gas pure.

Due to the high sensitivity of magnesium determinations the analyses are performed directly after dissolving the solid samples and appropriate dilution. The sole problem is the formation of involatile compounds. Compared with the other alkali earth elements, this danger is, however, smaller and its elimination easier. For instance, in an acetylene-air flame, phosphates have no depressive effect (17, 205) or only a slight one (84). In a coal gas-air flame the depressive effect is considerable (152) and some other elements are also active as interferents (114, 335). The resulting depression depends on the ratio with the interfering elements, as well as on the anions present in the solution. Evidently, the different phases formed in the crystallized particles may be very diverse.

The standard stock solutions may best be prepared by dissolving magnesium metal in the appropriate acid. Magnesium sulphate should not be used unless the solutions measured also contain sulphate anions. The interfering effects in the presence of chloride and sulphate anions differ (170, 220). Magnesium carbonate is unsuitable for the preparation of stock solutions, because it usually contains free magnesium hydroxide. The concentration must in this case be controlled, for instance, by chelatometry.

For the determination of magnesium concentration in blood serum (360) and other body liquids (362) the samples are aspirated directly after dilution and the addition of EDTA (10,000 ppm) strontium (5,000 ppm) (360), or lanthanum compounds (10,000 ppm) (362). The standard solution used contains magnesium and the added compound only.

When using a coal gas-air flame, the addition method must be used to eliminate the depressive influence of phosphates (152, 360). Another possible way is to incinerate the samples, redissolve them and use model standards and an addition of 500 ppm of strontium to the samples (174). Plant ash may be analysed similarly.

The determination of magnesium in rocks and other inorganic material is more complicated because of the many possible interfering elements. Aluminium and silicon are the two elements occuring most often. Silicate materials are usually decomposed with hydrofluoric and perchloric acids (sulphuric acid should be avoided because of the depressive effect of sulphates) so that silicon is removed. The effect of aluminium and the other interfering elements may be suppressed by strontium (33, 230, 259, 360), lanthanum (41, 294, 340, 362), calcium and oxine, lanthanum and oxine (294), or lanthanum and EDTA (12, 272). Using a nitrous oxide-acetylene flame all these precautions may be dispensed with (251).

For the analyses of metals and alloys, model standards are generally used (29, 33, 349) and/or the depressive effect is partly suppressed by the addition of oxine (349) or calcium (206). The samples are usually dissolved in acids. For aluminium, sodium hydroxide has also been used (349). For the determination of magnesium in cast iron and steels, 500 ppm strontium are added to eliminate the effect of the different variable aluminium contents (33). When determining magnesium in cathodic nickel, the variable content of silicon may be neglected, because nickel acts as a releasing element (29).

Calcium

Atomic absorption is not as advantageous for calcium as for magnesium. The sensitivity of 0·1 ppm is lower than that of emission flame photometry, but its main advantage is higher specificity. The resonance line at 422·7 nm lies near the visible region where emission of an acetylene-air flame is no longer negligible.

Hollow cathode lamps with calcium metal cathodes are generally used. Because calcium oxidizes easily on air, the cathode must be machined under a stream of oil (173). Sometimes a calcium-magnesium lamp is used (219).

For the preparation of stock solutions dehydrated calcium carbonate is most suitable.

To obtain the highest sensitivity the light beam should pass through the flame directly above the reaction zone, where the highest concentration of free atoms is attained. Above this narrow zone the concentration decreases again, due to the formation of calcium oxide. The value of this maximum concentration depends on the evaporation rate of the particular calcium compound. This evaporation rate decreases consecutively in calcium chloride, calcium nitrate and calcium sulphate. The chloride has a vapour pressure several orders of magnitude higher than the oxide, which results from the decomposition of calcium nitrate, and calcium oxide in its turn volatilizes much more easily than calcium sulphate. Above the reaction zone the differences are obscured by formation of the oxide. This reaction is controlled by the dissociation constant for the appropriate temperature and the partial pressure of oxygen in the flame gases.

The interference effects for calcium and strontium are more pronounced than for magnesium. However, the same procedures are used for their elimination. That is the releasing effect and the addition of organic compounds. Magnesium (82), 1,000 ppm strontium (84) and 10,000 ppm lanthanum (44, 340) have all been used as releasing elements. Organic compounds alone (359), or in combination with lanthanum have been tried (12, 294, 272). The interference effects are greater in the colder hydrogen-air (21) and coal gas-air flames (159).

Fuel rich flames with diffuse inner cones are often recommended (359). Using these the sensitivity is better and the localization of the light beam is not so critical.

The nitrous oxide-acetylene flame brings higher sensitivity and freedom from condensed phase interferences but more ionization occurs. According to MANNING (223) about 40% of the calcium atoms are ionized when spraying a 2 ppm solution. In the acetylene-air flame only slight ionization has been observed (82).

Calcium was determined in blood serum and other body liquids directly, after diluting the samples with an EDTA solution (359). For more precise measurements, deproteinization of the serum with trichloracetic acids in recommended. Urine may be analysed directly after dilution and addition of lanthanum (298). For the determination of calcium in rocks lanthanum was used as releasing element (20,000 ppm La) (340). In the presence of a 1% oxine solution 2,000 ppm La are sufficient to eliminate 400 ppm Al (294). RAMAKRISHNA, ROBINSON and WEST used 2,000 ppm Sr in the presence of 0·4 % EDTA solution, the concentration of interfering elements was, however, only up to 100 ppm (272). Similarly, ADAMS and PASSMORE succeeded in eliminating the depressive effect of 150 ppm Al by the addition of 1,000 ppm La in a solution of EDTA, which is 0·01 M finally (12).

Laboratory glassware contains considerable amounts of calcium. In the presence of traces of hydrofluoric acid, this may easily pass over into the solution. Hydrofluoric acid is often used for the decomposition of silicate materials. Complex fluorides are formed and these are only removed with great difficulty by fuming off with sulphuric or perchloric acids. After dilution with water, these complex fluorides hydrolyse and the hydrofluoric acid attacks the glass. Such solutions should always be stored in polythene bottles.

Strontium

Strontium is very similar to calcium in its behaviour. Its line at 460·7 nm has a sensitivity of 0·2 ppm which, because of the relatively low contents of strontium in natural materials, is rather poor. The detection limit is only about ten times better. The samples cannot be diluted much and the concentration of interfering elements is, therefore, usually higher than for calcium. Standard stock solutions are best prepared from strontium carbonate, but other salts may also be used (strontium chloride, strontium nitrate). So far only an acetylene-air flame and a modulated light signal have been used.

For the analysis of plant ash and soil extracts DAVID (87) recommends removing the phosphate anion, adding calcium for suppression of the aluminium interference, and using and addition method for evaluating the strontium content. TRENT and SLAVIN used and addition of 10,000 ppm

La for the analysis of the ashes of biological materials. The standard solutions contained only strontium and lanthanum. If however, the concentration of the phosphate anion exceeded 1,000 ppm an addition method was used. To suppress ionization 500 ppm sodium were added.

BELCHER (34) analysed coal ash by adding only 2,000 ppm lanthanum, the concentration of interfering elements being relatively low. For the analysis of rocks, model standard solutions prepared from dissolved standard rock samples were used (340) and 10,000 ppm La were added.

As for calcium, the simultaneous addition of some organic compounds lowers the concentration of the releasing element needed (12, 294).

The sensitivity in a nitrous oxide-acetylene flame is 0·06 ppm. The ionization degree may reach some 80% (27) but evidently no interferences in the condensed phase take place.

Barium

So far only few analytical papers dealing with barium have been published (12, 314). In an acetylene-air flame the sensitivity is relatively poor (5 ppm) because of the extremely low dissociation of barium oxide at this temperature. The situation is improved in the nitrous oxide-acetylene flame where a sensitivity of 0·4 ppm is achieved.

The greatest advantage of the absorption method is the specificity of determination. In emission flame photometry the resonance line Ba 553 nm coincides with the calcium molecular band at 554 nm. This band, however, only slightly absorbs the barium resonance line (66).

Hollow cathode lamps are generally used. A modulated light source is inevitable to eliminate both the barium line emission and especially the calcium band, because calcium is almost always present in the samples in excess.

The interference effects are similar to those of strontium (12) and in a nitrous oxide-acetylene flame will probably be less. The degree of ionization in this flame attains some 90 % for a 50 ppm solution (223) and so must be suppressed by the addition of alkali metals.

9.3 DETERMINATION OF NON-FERROUS METALS

Atomic absorption has perhaps made the biggest contribution to the measurement of elements in this group. For such elements as Cu, Ag, Zn, Cd, Hg, Sn, Pb, Bi and Sb, atomic absorption has resulted in great progress in the ease of their measurement because it is completely free from mutual interferences. The sensitivity, simplicity and speed of determination by atomic absorption in the case of Cu, Ag, Zn or Cd may be compared with the determination of sodium by emission flame photometry. No wonder then that in many laboratories atomic absorption replaces other methods of chemical analysis for these elements.

None of the elements in this group form involatile compounds and all dissociate readily even in relatively cool flames, i.e. city gas-air or propane-air flames. Their analytical resonance lines are found in the short wave ultra-violet spectrum region, so that the flame emission may be neglected. D.C. measuring devices may, therefore, be used. No specific interference effects are found and the overall composition of the samples analysed does not influence the results. Full advantage may, therefore, be taken of the high specificity of the atomic absorption measurement. Interference effects are limited to the influence of the overall concentration of salts in the solution sprayed and to the organic solvent effect, both of which only influence the amount of atoms reaching the flame (21). It is likely that in case of lead and tin only do some other processes also take place (for example, reactions with the flame gas components), as different flame profiles for aqueous and organic solutions suggest (76).

For all the elements mentioned absorption tubes may be used to considerably enhance the sensitivity of measurement. Another way to enhance sensitivity is to use enrichment of the elements concerned by extraction into organic solvents. The chelating reagent most often used is ammonium pyrrolidin dithiocarbamate (APDC) which makes possible the simultaneous extraction of approximately 14 elements from even acid solutions (215) — (see Table 9.6). Nitric acid, however, should be avoided because it decomposes APDC. Methyl isobutyl ketone (MIBK) is most frequently used as the organic solvent for extraction (20, 22, 40, 51, 56, 340), but several other solvents may be used, such as ethylacetate (20, 22, 214), methyl isopentyl ketone (242), methyl-n-amyl-ketone (365). All these can be sprayed directly into the flame. For copper, extraction of its diethyldithiocarbamate chelate into chloroform has been tried (41, 198). This solvent, however, is rather inconvenient, because on combustion poisonous phosgene may be formed.

Table 9.6

pH INTERVALS IN WHICH CHELATES WITH APDC* OF DIFFERENT
ELEMENTS ARE FORMED (215)

pH interval	Elements forming chelates
2–14	Ag Au Bi Cd Co Cu Fe Hg Ir Mn Ni Os Pb Pd Pt Ru Rh Tl Zn
2— 9	Sb Se
2— 8	Sn
2— 6	As Cr Mo Te V
2— 4	Nb U
2	W

* APDC — ammonium pyrrolidine dithiocarbamate

Analysis of blood sera and other body liquids is hindered by the inherently small concentration of non-ferrous metals (the serum of a healthy human individual contains some 1–1·2 ppm Cu and Zn). The serum cannot, therefore, be diluted to any great extent and the high protein content influences both the atomization process and the transport of aerosol into the flame. The samples must, therefore, be deproteinized before analysis. Because mineralization is slow, one prefers denaturation of proteins by trichloracetic acid and their removal by centrifuge. However, several non-ferrous metals are bound to the protein and must be released first, for example, by concentrated hydrochloric acid (154, 162). The supernatant liquid may then be sprayed directly into the flame.

If sufficient amounts of trichloracetic acid are added (5 ml to 1 ml serum), the release may be effected directly by the acid. After centrifuging the denaturated proteins, the supernatant liquid is placed into a

Table 9.7
REVIEW OF PAPERS DEALING WITH NON-FERROUS METALS

Elements determined				Material analysed	Note	Reference
mentioned in the chapter			other elements			
Cu				serum	extraction DDC	154
Cu	Zn		Fe	serum		317
	Zn			serum		162
Cu		Pb		blood, urine	extraction APDC	40
Cu				serum, urine, tissues	extraction EDTA	41
	Zn			serum, urine	absorption tube	121
	Zn		Mg	brain, tissue		73
	Hg			biological materials	absorption tube	115
		Pb		biological materials	absorption tube	278
Cu	Zn			biological materials		286
Cu	Zn		Fe Mg	plants		81
	Zn		Mg	chloroplasts		157
	Zn		Mn	tree leaves		55
Cu	Zn	Pb		wines		389
Cu				milk	extraction APDC	242
Cu				butter oil		366
Cu				sea water	extraction APDC	214
	Zn			agricultural materials	extraction APDC	22
	Zn		Ca Mg	animal nutrition	extraction APDC	259
Cu				agricultural materials	extraction APDC	20
	Hg			soil, rocks, gas		344
		Pb		gasoline		282
		Pb		gasoline		76

Table 9.7 continued I

Elements determined			Material analysed	Note	Refer-ence
mentioned in the chapter		other elements			
	Pb		gasoline		343
	Pb		gasoline		368
Cu			chemicals		168
Cu Zn	Pb	Fe	nickel-plating solutions		30
Hg			salts		269
	Sn		hydrogen per-oxide	absorption tube	13
Zn		Fe	glass		261
Cu Zn			silicates		39
Ag		Au Pd Pt Rh	ores		132
	Bi		sulphide mine-rals		294A
Cu			ores		319
Ag		Au	Pb-concentrates, metallurgical samples		143
Ag			Pb-concentrates		277
Ag			sulphide ores		293
Cd			ores, Zn-alloys		267
Ag		Au Pd Pt Rh	ores		132
Cu Zn	Pb		iron ore		326
Cu			Al-alloys, steel		348
Cu Zn			iron, aluminium		126
Cu			iron, steel		184
Cd			stainless steel		370
	Pb		steel, brass, bronze	extraction H_2PbI_4	77
Ag			Al-alloys		369
Zn			Al-alloys, bronze, brass		347
Zn			alloys		129
Cu Ag		Fe, Pd	gold		322
	Pb		Cu-alloys, steel		103

Table 9.7 continued II

| Elements determined | | Material analysed | Note | Reference |
mentioned in the chapter	other elements			
Cu		niobium, tantalum metal	extraction oxine	185
Zn		alloys		254
Cu Ag Zn	Ag Au Pd Pt Rh	study		235
Cu	Au	study		181
Cu Ag Cd	Au	study	absorption tube	390
Cu Zn	Mg Co Ni	study	absorption tube	120
Ag	Au Pd Pt Rh	study		208
Ag		study		37
Ag		study		180
Zn		study		105
Cd		study		78
Sn		study		68
Pb		study	absorption tube	72

APDC   Ammonium pyrrolidine dithiocarbamate
DDC   diethyldithiocarbamate
EDTA   ethylene diamine tetra-acetic acid

separating funnel, a chelating agent is added and the chelate is extracted into an organic solvent (40). When analysing urine, the extraction has to be performed in an acid medium (pH = 4·5), otherwise calcium phosphate is precipitated and several heavy metals are lost from the solution (365).

For the analysis of plants (55, 81, 259), milk (242) and wine (389), the samples are commonly mineralized by incineration or by wet ashing with acids.

In metals and alloys these elements are frequently present in somewhat higher concentrations and these materials may, therefore, be analysed directly after solution in appropriate acids.

Usually 0·5–1 gm samples are dissolved and filled up to volumes of 50 or 100 ml. However, the resulting concentration of salts (0·5–2%) may influence the atomization process and thus also the values measured. This effect may be eliminated by using standard solutions with the corresponding amount of dissolved metal, but irrespective of the minor components which do not affect the analysis.

When analysing silicate materials, the overall salt concentration in atomized solution is usually lower because the main component, i.e. silica, is fumed off with hydrofluoric acid. If however, the content of the analyte is too low, extraction with APDC is recommended in certain cases (340).

Standard solutions for analytical curves are usually prepared by the dilution of stock standard solutions. These in their turn are best prepared by dissolving high purity metals in suitable acids, usually nitric. For tin, sulphuric acid is preferable. A review of analytical work on non-ferrous metal determinations is given in Table 9.7.

Copper

The determination of copper concentrations by atomic absorption presents no problems. All compounds dissociate readily (in an acetylene-air flame about 80% of copper is present as free atoms and the remaining 20% mostly as CuH or CuOH, the formation of which influence the flame profile). In propane-air flames, when spraying aqueous solutions, maximum absorption is reached in the upper part of the flame. With organic solvents maximum absorption is in the lower part (214). On the whole, however, the absorption is not very dependent on the height of the light beam in the flame.

The manufacture of hollow cathode lamps is easy; the cathode can be made of copper or brass. Argon, neon or helium can be used as the filler gas. Helium has some advantages (184), because due to its smaller sputtering properties the current intensity may be increased considerably without reducing the sensitivity. This is an improvement over argon filled lamps. Copper is also present in several multi-element lamps (227, 300).

Of the two copper resonance lines at 324·8 nm and 327·4 nm, the former is usually measured with higher sensitivity. In aqueous solutions the sensitivity reached is about 0·1 ppm, in organic solvent solutions it is about double. The high stability and high brightness of copper hollow cathode lamps make the use of large scale expansion possible, so that a detection limit of 0·005 ppm may be reached (263).

Extraction with APDC is often used for the analysis of some materials. The copper chelate is very stable and extraction proceeds even from strong acid solutions (6N HCl and 9N H_2SO_4) — (20).

Silver

The atomic absorption determination of silver is so precise and reliable that it often replaces the fire assay methods used since the Middle Ages. In the flame, silver is completely dissociated and its flame profile does not change even when using organic solvents. The absolute concentration of free silver atoms in flame gases may only be influenced by changes in atomization and transportation yields.

Interference effects are caused by a considerable excess of some cations (e.g. thorium, tungsten). These form refractory oxides blocking the evaporation of silver in to the flame, and by some anions precipitating silver in solution. For 0·05 molar solutions of various interfering compounds the following absorption decreases have been reported (37): iodate 80%, permanganate 15%, tungsten 6%, thorium 15%. The influence of halides depends on the time which elapses between the addition of interferent and the measurement. As a rule, colloid solutions are formed and no decrease is observed, because silver halides dissociate easily in the flame. However, on standing silver halides are precipitated and absorbed on the walls of the flask and the concentration decreases progressively. Because chloride anions are a common impurity, all solutions and reagents used must be scrupulously free of them. This means that bi-distilled water and electronically pure-grade reagents should be used. The effect of chloride anions may be successfully masked by the addition of mercury (293).

The two main silver resonance lines are at 326·1 nm and 338·2 nm, of which the former is usually measured with a sensitivity of 0·1 ppm.

If the hollow cathode also emits a copper spectrum, care must be taken to isolate the silver line at 328·1 nm from the copper resonance line at 327·4 nm, as otherwise the copper content in the solution sprayed may influence the results. The sensitivity of silver may be considerably enhanced by using absorption tubes.

Zinc

The determination of zinc contents by atomic absorption offers considerable advantages, which is the reason why so far, apart from the measurement of magnesium concentrations, it has been most frequently studied.

Zinc compounds dissociate completely in the flame and, therefore, no major interferences are observed. The resonance line at 213·8 nm (giving a sensitivity of 0·04 ppm) lies far into the ultra violet region where glass and even silica may absorb light. The silica windows for hollow cathode lamps should, therefore, be selected according to their transparency, since individual windows can differ widely due to differing amounts of traces of iron in the silica material.

Hollow cathodes for zinc lamps are often prepared from brass, but due to preferential cathodic sputtering of zinc such lamps degenerate into copper lamps after some time. An intermetallic compound of calcium and zinc has been recommended as more suitable (346). Helium (124) and neon (346) are preferred as filler gas.

At the wavelength of the zinc line the flame gases absorb considerably (a 10 cm acetylene-air flame some 40%), and the absorption varies with flame composition. The gas flow should, therefore, be carefully watched. Due to the omnipresence of zinc in the spectrometer parts and the high sensitivity of its determination, spraying just pure acid solution may cause absorption. This is usually caused by zinc being dissolved from the metallic parts of the sprayer-burner. To avoid these effects the metal parts should be shielded with suitable plastic material (389).

Because of the short wavelength of the zinc line, light scattering from unevaporated salt particles may present some problems (317). Elimination of these interferences has already been described (see Chapter 9).

When using an absorption tube, a depressive effect due to phosphates was observed. This was evidently caused by incomplete evaporation of the salt particles because a hydrogen-air flame with low temperature and a Beckman direct sprayer-burner were used in this case.

Cadmium

The problems of the determination of cadmium concentrations are identical to those of zinc. The determination is somewhat easier because at the Cd line (228·8 nm), the absorption of the flame gases for a 10 cm acetylene-air flame is only 25%. On the other hand, cadmium is a much less common element and generally a higher sensitivity is required. The sensitivity for the Cd resonance line at 228·8 nm is the same as for zinc (0·04 ppm). Cadmium may also be easily determined with absorption tubes. This technique has been applied to the determination of cadmium in uranium compounds (333). Uranium was separated by extraction of U(VI) in 5N nitric acid solution with tributyl phosphate in kerosene. Vapour discharge lamps have sometimes been used as line sources (31, 200).

Mercury

Mercury has a unique position due to its high volatility at room temperature. Atomic absorption has been used since the early thirties for its determination (381). All monitors indicating the mercury concentration in the atmosphere are based on this principle. Although from this point of view the properties of mercury are ideal, the sensitivity of determination is rather poor because the resonance line at 185·0 nm lies in the Schumann region with strong oxygen absorption. The Hg line at 254 nm corresponding to a forbidden transition between a triplet and singlet state with forty times smaller oscillator strength must be used instead. The resulting sensitivity is about 10 ppm. Mercury discharge lamps are generally used as light sources.

Due to its extreme volatility absorption tubes may be used to full advantage (115). In some cases, when stannous chloride is added to the solution sprayed as a reducing agent, a very small flame is sufficient for the complete atomization of mercury (268). Eventually the flame may be disposed with altogether (269). So far mercury has been determined in biological materials after extraction with dithizone into MIBK (365), using absorption tubes (115, 189), and also in geological materials (344).

Tin

At the present time tin presents the greatest difficulty of all the elements in the group. It probably forms stable oxides which are difficult to dissociate. Also the sensitivity is relatively poor. A strongly reducing luminous acetylene flame is, therefore, recommended (124). However, the best sensitivity may be attained in a hydrogen-air flame. Using this flame, the sensitivity is about three times better than with the acetylene one, and marginally better than the acetylene-nitrous oxide flame (27).

Recently the line at 224·6 nm has been recommended instead of the originally proposed 286·3 nm and 235·5 nm lines (68). However, if the line at 224·6 nm is to be used, the cathode must emit no copper spectrum, otherwise the 224·7 and 224·4 copper lines may interfere.

Tin has a very low vapour pressure at its melting point. Cup-shaped hollow cathodes in which tin is in a molten state during the operation of the lamp are, therefore, recommended. This seems an easier way to increase the brightness of the tin spectrum than by using auxiliary boosting electrodes as in standard high brightness lamps (68).

So far the highest sensitivity (0·025 ppm) has been attained by AGGAZZI (13) using absorption tubes and an oxy-hydrogen flame. For a 10 cm luminous acetylene-air flame the sensitivity is usually only some 10 ppm.

No specific interfering effects have been reported. However, by analogy with other oxide-forming elements, difficulties may be expected in this respect.

Lead

From the atomic absorption point of view, lead resembles the elements of the first and second subgroup of the periodic table more than tin. With argon-filled hollow cathode lamps, and using the Pb line at

283·3 nm, a sensitivity of 1 ppm has been attained. SLAVIN and MANNING (313) have demonstrated that neon is better as filler gas because the more sensitive line at 217·0 nm may then be used. This line interferes with the argon ion line Ar II 217·14 nm, and consequently cannot be used with argon filled lamps.

According to some authors the use of low temperature flames brings a higher sensitivity. DAGNALL and WEST (76) point out that with a low temperature propane-air flame the height of the light beam above the burner top is important. Best results are obtained with the light passing immediately above the burner slot. CHAKRABARTI, ROBINSON and WEST (72) attained the highest sensitivity by using a total consumption burner with a T-piece adapter and a "reversed flame" (i.e. atomizing the sample with hydrogen instead of oxygen). A more reducing atmosphere is thus provided, which enhances the lead absorption by a factor of 3·5 and attains a sensitivity of 0·013 ppm.

In a propane-air flame only slight depressive effects with beryllium, aluminium, thorium, zirconium and phosphate ions have been reported (76). They are probably due to the mechanical trapping of the lead atoms in the unevaporated particles. In the reversed oxy-hydrogen flame (72), depressive effects of several anions (especially the carbonate and iodide anions) have been found. These, however, can easily be overcome by the addition of EDTA (72). Using absorption tubes and a hydrogen-air flame, a depressive effect with sulphates has also been observed (294B).

Lead is most often required to be determined in metallurgical and biochemical samples and in gasoline as an anti-explosive additive. The determination of lead concentrations in serum and urine is important because of its toxicity. For the analysis of urine WILLIS (365) suggests extraction at pH values between 3 and 4. This value should be adjusted by the addition of acetic acid. The standard solutions are prepared by extraction of corresponding amounts of lead from known aqueous solutions. Metallic lead is best used for the preparation of the stock solution.

Lead in gasoline may be determined after dilution with iso-octane 1 : 10 (196) and the standards are prepared by dilution of tetraethyl lead with iso-octane (76, 343).

Antimony

So far very little is known about antimony. The Sb 231·1 nm and Sb 217·6 nm lines have been recommended. The latter is more sensitive, giving a sensitivity of about 1 ppm (263).

Bismuth

For the determination of bismuth the 223·1 nm line is most sensitive (0·5 ppm), the next is the Bi line at 222·8 nm which is about half as sensitive (294A). The Bi 306·8 nm line is several times less sensitive and lies in the region of the strong absorption bands of hydroxyl radicals (263, 365). The sensitivity according to GATEHOUSE and WILLIS (124) is improved in low temperature flames. The fuel to oxidant ratio has no pronounced effect on the absorption of bismuth.

For the determination of bismuth contents in steels (232), iron is extracted from a hydrochloric acid solution by isobutyl acetate and the concentration of bismuth in the aqueous layer is then determined. The sensitivity reached is 0·0005% Bi in low alloy steels. This sensitivity deteriorates with increasing concentration of the alloying elements, because these may not be extracted by isobutyl acetate (e.g. nickel and chromium).

9.4 THE DETERMINATION OF NOBLE METALS

At present relatively little is known about the reactions of noble metal atoms in a flame. Not until the advent of atomic absorption were measurements on most of these elements in the flame possible, so that no experience from emission flame photometry could be exploited.

Noble metals may roughly be divided into three groups. (a) Gold and palladium, which are most easily accessible to atomic absorption determinations. Both are easily atomized in the flame and are not subject to any specific interference effects, so that their determination is sensitive and without complications. (b) Platinum, rhodium and ruthenium, which may also be determined, but with these several specific interference effects have been observed, especially in low temperature flames (323). (c) Iridium and osmium, the measurement of which is possible (26) but little is known about the interfering effects. In an acetylene-air flame specific interferences may be expected.

The main difficulty in determining all noble metals is the extremely low concentration in which they are usually present in most materials. This makes chemical enrichment unavoidable. It may be accomplished by cupellation, by co-precipitation with some metal sulphides (132), by the ion-exchange technique or by cementation with magnesium or zinc powder. Several ion extraction systems have also been proposed, whereas among the chelating reagents chinolin-selenol-2 should be mentioned. A review of the published papers is in Table 9.8.

Table 9.8

REVIEW OF PAPERS DEALING WITH NOBLE METALS

Elements determined					Material analysed	Reference
Au				Ag	Pb-concentrates, metallurgical samples	143
Au					ores	63
Au					ores	257
Au					ores	303
Au					ores	338
Au	Pd	Pt	Rh	Ag	ores	132
Au					mill cyanide solutions	305
Au					cyanide waste solutions	325
Au	Pd	Pt	Rh		alloys	323
	Pd			Ag Cu Fe	gold	322
	Pd				Pt-alloys	106
Au	Pd	Pt	Rh		study	208
Au	Pd	Pt	Rh	Mg Cu Ag Zn	study	235
Au				Cu	study	181
Au				Ag Cd Cu	study	390
		Rh			study	148
			Ir		study	247

NORTHWEST MISSOURI STATE
UNIVERSITY LIBRARY
MARYVILLE, MISSOURI 64468

Gold

Gold is often determined by atomic absorption because it is a relatively common metal. Also the control of the ore flotating and processing requires a great number of analyses, so that the speed and simplicity of atomic absorption spectrometry come into full use. An automatic analyser has been built for the analysis of waste solutions from the cyanide process (63). To overcome any changes in the vaporization and transportation processes, palladium has been added as internal standard. The hollow cathode lamp emitted gold and palladium lines and their ratio was measured.

Gold may be enriched by extraction of the chloride complex (63) or the bromide complex (143, 338) into MIBK. Co-precipitation with lead sulphide or copper sulphide (132) has also been used. From the ore, gold samples may be digested with a hot solution of sodium cyanide (257, 303). Concentrations down to 0·03 gm/ton may be determined in this way.

Using the Au 242·8 nm line, the sensitivity is about 0·5 ppm. Using an extraction of the bromide complex this corresponds to a concentration of 1 gm/ton (338).

Gold has been determined in alloys and metallic beads after cupellation. In low temperature coal gas-air flames blocking effects by several metals (Cu, Zn) have been observed. Free atoms of gold have a relatively long lifetime in the flame (390), so that absorption tubes may be used with advantage (292).

Palladium

Palladium contents may be measured as easily as gold. No specific interference effects have been observed. Sensitivity is about 1 ppm when using the Pd 247·6 nm line. High concentration levels of salts may cause a blocking effect. For chemical enrichment co-precipitation with lead and copper sulphide (132), extraction of the pyridine complex $Pd(C_6H_5N)_2(SCN)_2$ into MIBK (106) or cupellation have been used. To enhance the sensitivity of determination absorption tubes may also be used. The high silver concentration in the solution sprayed (originating from the silver beads 5,000 ppm Ag) caused a blocking effect with absorption tubes. This could be overcome by heating the tube (292).

Ruthenium, rhodium and platinum

So far no analytical work on ruthenium has been published, but it may be expected that ruthenium will be similar in its behaviour to rhodium and platinum. The determination of the last two is somewhat more difficult than the measurement of palladium and gold. Numerous specific interference effects have been observed in the low temperature coal gas-air flame. Some acids, especially sulphuric acid and the other metals of the platinum group (Os, Ir) and even several common metals (Cu, Zn, Sn, Ni) influence the absorption of these elements (323). In the hotter acetylene-air flame these effects are probably less pronounced or totally absent. Analytical work has so far been concerned mostly with pure solutions. The sensitivities of the recommended lines are : Pt at 265·9 nm 2 ppm, Rh at 343·6 nm 0·3 ppm and Ru at 349·9 nm also 0·3 ppm. The use of absorption tubes enhances the sensitivity of rhodium, but for platinum the enhancement factor is slight (292).

Iridium and osmium

The sensitivities of different iridium lines have been investigated and different results reported. According to MULFORD (247) the most sensitive line at 285·0 nm has a sensitivity of 35 ppm but a sensitivity of 12 ppm has been found for Ir 263·4 nm (26). For osmium, a nitrous oxide-acetylene flame secures a slightly better sensitivity (26).

9.5 THE DETERMINATION OF FERROUS METALS

Besides iron, we may include cobalt, nickel, chromium, manganese and molybdenum in this group. All these elements have several common features. All have line rich spectra (especially iron, cobalt and nickel), and with the exception of iron all are used as alloying elements in steels.

The sensitivities of concentration determinations reported by different authors often disagree and sometimes even non resonance lines, corresponding to transitions from metastable states are recommended. This disagreement in the sensitivities reported may be explained by the difficulties of isolating a single line from the line-rich spectrum emitted by the hollow cathode lamp. The use of high-brightness hollow cathode lamps for iron, cobalt and nickel is, therefore, preferable.

No specific interference effects have been observed for iron, cobalt and nickel; for chromium and manganese the effects are only slight; for molybdenum they may be considerable. The tendency to have interference effects corresponds to the tendency to form oxides in the flame and is, therefore, predominantly due to the formation of non-volatile compounds and may be eliminated by using releasing elements. Thus, for example, the reported depressive effect of silicon on chromium and manganese may be eliminated by the addition of calcium (265, 357) or strontium (315A) to the solution sprayed.

For chromium and manganese slightly reducing flames are recommended, but the presence of high amounts of nickel and also probably iron makes the difference between an oxidizing and reducing flame disappear (99). For molybdenum a strongly reducing luminous acetylene-air or a nitrous oxide-acetylene flame are recommended (186).

All the elements mentioned are important alloying constituents of steels. The sensitivity of atomic absorption spectrometry is usually sufficient to allow their determination after simply dissolving the sample. Most often a mixture of hydrochloric and nitric acids is used. Sometimes sulphuric acid and phosphoric acids with several drops of nitric acid to facilitate oxidation are preferred (36). In any case, the volume of acids in all the solutions sprayed must be kept constant, because generally the acids have a depressive effect. Nitric acid has the smallest effect. Iron is usually also added to the standard solutions to imitate the samples. Sometimes ammonium chloride is used as a buffer, and then the addition of iron is superfluous (32, 245).

For the analysis of organic materials (e.g. plants, faeces) the ash is often digested with acids and the undissolved residue is filtered off (81, 88, 357). A similar treatment has been used for fertilizers (230). If chemical

Table 9.9

REVIEW OF PAPERS DEALING WITH FERROUS METALS

Elements determined						Material analysed	Reference
		Fe			Cu Zn	serum	317
		Fe				urine	393
				Ni		urine	316
				Ni		biological materials	286
	Mn	Fe				plants	18
			Co	Ni		plants	19
	Mn	Fe				plants	88
		Fe			Cu Mg Zn	plants	81
	Mn				Zn	free leaves	55
	Mo					water, plants, silicates	65
Cr						faeces	357
			Co	Ni		water	56
	Mn	Fe				sea water	175
Cr	Mo					sea water	94
	Mo					phosphates	388
	Mo					superphosphates, steel	86
				Ni		cracking feedstocks	179
				Ni		cracking feedstocks	341
		Fe				tetraphenyl reactor coolant	240
		Fe	Co	Ni		asphaltic fraction of sediments	57
				Ni	Zn	Ni/Al_2O_3 catalysts	166
		Fe				glass	261
	Mo					niobium and tantalum metal	187
				Ni		steel	183
	Mo					alloy steels	186
Cr						iron, steel	182
Cr						steel	32
	Mo					Fe-alloys	245
	Mn					steel	36
			Co			steel, nickel	231
Cr	Mn				Mg	Ni-alloys	29
Cr	Mn				Mg	Ni-alloys	99
Cr				Ni		Al—Cr—Ni-alloys	193
		Fe			Cu Ag Pd	gold	322

Table 9.9 continued

Elements determined			Material analysed	Refer-ence
Fe			tungstencarbide	35
Fe		Cu Zn Pb	nickel-plating solutions	302
Mo		Sr	study	83
	Co Ni	Mg Cu Zn	study	120
Cr			study	112

al enrichment is necessary, extraction of the APDC chelate into MIBK is often used.

A special group of materials analysed are crude and lubricating oils. Nickel, vanadium and iron act as poisons on cracking catalysts. Also the content of trace elements in lubricating oils indicate the wear of certain mechanical parts of the engines. Their determination is, therefore, an important part of prevention. To eliminate the tedious mineralization of the samples, they are analysed directly after dilution with some non-polar solvent, usually xylene (233, 314) or MIBK (58). The fuel flow of the burner must be adequately reduced to compensate for this additional fuel. The standard solutions are best prepared by using metallo-organic compounds or metal naphthenates.

The procedure recommended by MEANS and RATCLIFF (233) is as follows: naphthenic acid is neutralized with ammonia and dissolved in water. An aqueous solution of the particular element is added and the naphthenate formed is extracted into xylene. The content of this stock solution is then controlled after re-extraction into diluted nitric acid (1 : 1) by comparing with aqueous standard solutions. This procedure has been used for the preparation of silver, copper, tin, magnesium and lead solutions. Difficulties have been encountered with chromium because its naphthenate is not easily extracted into xylene quantitatively. Table 9.9 gives a review of papers dealing with ferrous metals and the materials analysed.

Chromium

The most sensitive 357·9 nm chromium line is used with neon-filled hollow cathode lamps giving a sensitivity of about 0·2 ppm. With argon-filled lamps the argon line at 357·8 nm may interfere and a better sensitivity is attained with the Cr 359·3 nm line (182). The sensitivity of the latter is only some 25% worse.

Several interference effects have been observed. The depressive effect of silicon may be suppressed by calcium (265). For very low chromium contents depressive effects with nickel and tungsten (from 500 ppm upwards) and molybdenum (from 100 ppm upwards) have been reported (182). The effect of iron is corrected for either by adding the same amount to the standard solutions or more simply by using an ammonium chloride buffer. Standard solutions are made as follows: To 1 gm sample dissolved in a 1 : 4 ratio by volume of HNO_3-HCl mixture, are added 2 gm of ammonium chloride in a 100 ml volume. The standard solution then contains only chromium and ammonium chloride (32). Using this buffer the interference effects are better eliminated in a nonluminous flame. Other workers (182) recommend a slightly fuel-rich flame with a diffuse inner cone. Chromate salts are generally used for the preparation of standard solutions. For trace determinations the extractions of Cr (VI) from cold hydrochloric acid solutions into MIBK may be used. If Cr (III) is present, this must be oxidized with permanganate first (112).

Molybdenum

Molybdenum has a somewhat richer spectrum. With the recommended Mo 313·26 nm line a sensitivity of 0·5 ppm has been reached in a fuel-rich flame. The sensitivity depends greatly on the exact region where the light beam passes through the flame. For optimum sensitivity only a small region exactly above the reaction zone should be used. The exact height depends on the fuel to oxidant ratio (124).

Using a strongly luminous flame the noise may be too high so that some authors prefer the less sensitive Mo line at 379·83 nm (245). Its sensitivity is about half that of the previous line.

Using a total consumption burner with a graphite premixing channel and alcoholic solutions, a detection limit of 0·03 ppm has been reached (188), as compared with 0·1 ppm for a laminar flame.

When determining concentrations of molybdenum several interference effects take place. A depressive effect due to calcium, strontium and manganese has been reported by DAVID (86). It depends strongly on the anions present and may be partly eliminated by the addition of phosphates or aluminium. In the presence of 2,000 ppm aluminium, the interference effects are reduced to about 10% of their previous values. MOSTYN and CUNNINGHAM (245) recommend ammonium chloride as an interference suppressor for the analysis of steels. In this work the standard solution contained only molybdenum and ammonium chloride.

Because of the complicated interference effects, KIRKBRIGHT, SMITH and WEST (186) recommend the use of a nitrous oxide-acetylene flame. Although the sensitivity, compared with a luminous acetylene-air flame, is not considerably increased, the method is free of interference effects, with the exception of those due to the total iron content in the solutions.

For the chemical enrichment of low molybdenum contents in niobium and tantalum metals, extraction of the molybdenum (VI) by 8-hydroxy-quinolinate into butanol (187), and the APDC chelate into MIBK from aqueous solutions, plants and rocks (65) have been used.

Manganese

With the manganese 279·5 nm line a sensitivity of 0·05 ppm is attained. The Mn line at 403·07 is sometimes used giving a lower sensitivity (43). In a reducing flame the sensitivity is somewhat higher but several interference effects are more pronounced. According to BELCHER (36), iron has a depressive effect in a reducing flame, but no such effect was observed in a stoichiometric flame. On the contrary, chromium (2,000 ppm) enhanced the manganese absorption more in a stoichiometric and less in a reducing flame. The interference effect of chromium was diminished by using a narrower light beam or by increasing the burner slot width. Similar observations for the interference effect of silicon are reported by other authors (315A). All these intriguing effects may be explained by taking into account the fact that the outer layers of the flame, where the temperature is lower and the dissociation equilibria shifted, influence the measurement less if the light beam passes only through the inner parts of the flame.

Manganese is usually determined directly after dissolving the samples. For the preparation of the stock solution, metallic manganese or manganese dioxide may be used.

Iron

The determination of iron presents no difficulties. Most often the Fe 248·3 nm line with a sensitivity of 0·1 ppm is recommended, but several other lines may be found suitable. So far no interfering effects have been observed in an acetylene-air flame. In a coal gas-air flame a depressive effect of silicon has been reported (4).

Iron is a common element and due to its relatively high concentration, its concentration may easily be determined directly after dissolving the sample. On the other hand, when determining trace amounts of iron in high purity materials the danger of contamination is rather high and the "blank" value of the whole analytical procedure should be carefully determined (i.e. identical conditions except no iron present).

A stock solution is best prepared by dissolving iron metal in a suitable acid.

Cobalt

The determination of cobalt is somewhat more difficult because its content in the materials analysed is generally much lower. Otherwise cobalt and iron are rather similar in their behaviour. The choice of the analytical line may differ according to the conditions used. According to HARRISON (146), the most sensitive cobalt line is at 240·72 nm, demanding high resolving power instruments. However, in most cases this line interferes with the non-absorbing Co line at 240·77 nm. The relative intensity of the latter increases with increasing hollow cathode lamp current. At about 15 mA this parasitic radiation outweighs the gain due to higher sensitivity, so that several other lines may prove more sensitive. With the 242·49 nm, 252·14 nm or 241·15 nm lines a sensitivity of 0·5 ppm is attained. When using high-brightness hollow cathode lamps this problem is eliminated.

Table 9.10

REVIEW OF PAPERS DEALING WITH THE DETERMINATION OF FIVE
AND MORE ELEMENTS IN DIFFERENT MATERIALS

Material analysed	Elements determined	Reference
blood serum	K Mg Ca Cu Zn	125
urine	Zn Cd Hg Pb Bi Ni	365
beer	Na K Ca Cu Fe	117
water	Na K Mg Ca Cu Fe	62
water, sediments from water	Mg Ca Cu Zn Mn Fe Ni	265
sea water	Cu Zn Mn Fe Ni	107
brine	Cu V Cr Mo Mn Co Ni	224
rocks, minerals	Na K Rb Mg Ca Sr Cd Fe Co Ni	44
rocks, minerals	Mg Ca Sr Cu Fe	340
sulphide ores	Cu Zn Pb Co Ni Pd	134
lubricating oils	Mg Cu Ag Sn Pb Cr Fe Ni Al	233
lubricating oils	Na Ba Cu Ag Pb Cr Fe Ni	314
cement	Na K Mg Ca Mn	335
fertilizers	Mg Cu Zn Mn Fe	230
Al and Cu alloys	Na Mg Sr Ag Cd Pb Co	110
Al alloys	Ci Mg Cu Cd Zn Cr Mn Fe Ni	37A
Cu alloys, gold	Cu Ag Zn Pb Fe Ni	64
gold	Cu Ag Zn Pb Fe	299
cast iron, steel	Mg Cu Cr Mn Ni	43
Mg and Al alloys	Ca Cu Zn Mn Fe	225
sodium	Cu Zn Pb Mn Fe Ni	52
metalurgical samples	Mg Cd Pb Bi Co	232
iron, steel	Mg Cu Mn Co Ni	315A
non-ferrous alloys	K Mg Ca Cu Ag Zn Cd Pb Sb Bi Mn Fe Ni In Te	297

Cobalt contents have been determined in steels and nickel (231, 315A), in silicates, and in brines after extraction with APDC. For the analysis of water, cobalt and nickel were enriched by a two stage process. Both were co-precipitated onto iron hydroxide and iron was then extracted from a hydrochloric acid solution with isopropyl-ether. From the aqueous layer Co and Ni were then extracted with APDC into MIBK. The resulting enrichment factor was 1,000 (56). The stock solution can best be prepared by dissolving cobalt metal in a suitable acid.

Nickel

The problems of the determination of nickel contents are similar to those of cobalt. So far no interference effects have been observed (183). Nickel contents may be determined either directly or after extraction with the APDC-MIBK method. The sensitivity of the 232·0 nm line is about 0·2 ppm. WILLIS (365) recommends the Ni line at 341·5 nm. This is about 25 % less sensitive, but is not disturbed by the non-absorbing Ni lines at 231·7 nm and 232·1 nm. KINSON and BELCHER (183) use the more sensitive line, but to straighten the analytical curves they substract the transmission corresponding to the parasite lines, i.e. they subtract the deflection when spraying a 5,000 ppm nickel solution, because at this level they assume the 232·0 nm line is completely absorbed, so that the whole deflection is given by the parasite lines.

The stock solution may best be prepared by dissolving the metal.

9.6 THE DETERMINATION OF GALLIUM, INDIUM AND THALLIUM

Concentrations of these three elements may be relatively easily determined by atomic absorption. They dissociate readily in a flame and have previously been determined by emission flame photometry. The sensitivity of the measurements of these elements by absorption is not very good. The recommended lines and their appropriate sensitivities are: Ga 287·4 nm 2·5 ppm, In 304·0 nm 1 ppm and Tl 276·8 nm 0·8 ppm.

Gallium and indium have extremely low melting points and very low vapour pressures. Cup-shaped cathodes made of niobium and titanium respectively are, therefore, recommended (246). High-frequency electrodeless discharge tubes may also be used. So far no specific interference effects have been reported (297). Indium contents have been determined in InSb alloys (8).

For thallium, vapour discharge tubes are often used. An exit window must be cut into the protecting glass bulb. No interference effects have been observed. For the determination of thallium in blood serum and urine a detection limit of 0·2 ppm has been found (308). This can be further diminished to 0·05 ppm using absorption tubes (189). For chemical enrichm entextraction of the dithizonate into MIBK has been used (189).

9.7 THE DETERMINATION OF ARSENIC, SELENIUM AND TELLURIUM

These elements also have relatively low melting points, but their vapour pressures are much higher than for gallium and indium. Normal cylindrical hollow cathodes are generally used in lamps. The lamps must be supplied with a low electric current, otherwise the elements vaporize too quickly, condense on the cooler parts of the lamp and are thus lost from the cathode. The life time of these lamps is, therefore, relatively short.

A major nuisance when determining concentrations of arsenic, selenium and tellurium is the short wavelength of their most sensitive lines. All are in the extreme ultraviolet region where the flame gases absorb considerably, so that high intensity light signals are required. For selenium, a graphite hollow cathode impregnated with selenium vapour in vacuum, has been used (275). For tellurium, an aluminium cathode has proved better than a copper one (135). Radio or microwave frequency electrodeless discharge tubes may bring some advantages because of their higher brightness.

The three most sensitive arsenic lines are at 189·0, 193·7 and 197·2 nm. The first is the most sensitive. However, for analytical work the second, having a sensitivity of 2 ppm, is recommended (311). Non-selective background absorption may be measured and corrected using the argon line at 199 nm. Arsenic contents have so farbeen measured in glass, gold alloys, plants and soil extracts (311).

The recommended line for selenium is at 196·0 nm which has a sensitivity of 2 ppm. The other two possible lines at 204·0 and 206·3 nm are much less sensitive. Selenium contents has been measured in soils and plants (275). Using a T-shaped flame adapter the sensitivity may be increased and the noise due to the flame absorption lowered (275). The same evidently also holds for tellurium.

Selenium has been jointly measured with tellurium in copper metal (315). The copper was dissolved in nitric acid and the solution sprayed directly into the flame. The observed blocking effect of the copper was eliminated by adding copper to the standard solutions. By dissolving 1 gm of copper in 50 ml of solution a concentration of 0·005% Se and 0·0005% Te could be estimated. The tellurium Te 214·2 nm line has a sensitivity of 1 ppm. Using absorption tubes this could be enhanced to 0·02 ppm. Tellurium was enriched by extraction of the diethyldithiocarbamate complex into benzene (189).

9.8 THE DETERMINATION OF REFRACTORY ELEMENTS

This group comprises the following elements: Be, B, Al, Sc, Y, the rare earths, Si, Ge, Ti, Zr, Hf, Th, V, Nb, Ta, W, U and Re. The laminar nitrous oxide-acetylene flame is predominantly used for their determination, although absorption spectra of these elements may also be observed in a laminar oxygen-nitrogen-acetylene flame or a strongly reducing oxy-acetylene flame.

The use of nitric oxide, suggested by WILLIS (367), instead of nitrous oxide as an oxidant (because of its higher oxygen content) brought some sensitivity enhancement, but due to the higher noise level of the nitric oxide-acetylene flame the detection limit did not improve markedly (221, 313A). Nitric oxide is a highly corrosive toxic gas, several times more expensive than nitrous oxide and, therefore, no general use may be expected.

The use of nitrous oxide-acetylene flames has some special features which should be mentioned. In general, the setting of conditions for achieving optimum sensitivity is far more critical than with common air-acetylene or air-coal gas flames. Even small departures from optimum may cause severe loss of sensitivity.

Among the conditions required to maintain optimum sensitivity, the fuel to oxidant ratio, the light path position and sometimes even the solution uptake are important. The fuel to oxidant ratio is indicaled by the height of the red zone (the so-called "red feather"). For fuel-rich flames this red zone is 25–40 mm high, in oxidant rich flames only about 5 mm.

For fuel-rich flames the emission of the flame may reduce the signal to noise ratio for a given measurement. This may be improved by increasing the hollow cathode lamp current, only to the point, however, where the absorption begins to decrease, or the recommended maximum lamp current is reached. The emission spectrum of a nitrous oxide-acetylene flame shows CN bands with heads at 421·6 nm, 388·3 nm and 359·0 nm and NH bands with heads at 336 nm and CH bands at 314·3 nm. Below 300 nm the emission is weak. Strong emission bands appear between 560 and 750 nm. No elements are however, measured in this region with the nitrous oxide-acetylene flame (223 A).

The light beam should pass through the flame some 5–10 mm above the burner. Higher up, better freedom from interference effects is found, but some sensitivity is lost (27). The sensitivities in the nitrous oxide-acetylene flame are given in Table 8.1 on page 104. The disagreement often encountered among findings of different authors, is partly due to the extreme dependence on the conditions set, and partly to the variable quality of hollow cathode lamps for these elements, since they were not produced commercially until recently. This situation may well be illustrated by comparing the sensitivity data for the rare earth elements according to several authors, which are collected in Table 9.11. Therefore when determining rare earth elements it is advisable to measure the sensitivity of different lines and find out which is best for the particular conditions used.

The temperature of the acetylene-nitrous oxide flame is so high (2,955°C, see table 2.1) that ionization of elements with ionization energies

Table 9.11

SENSITIVITY DATA ON RARE EARTH DETERMINATIONS IN A N_2O—C_2H_2 FLAME

Element	Perkin, Elmer (263)			Anderson (28)			Amos, Willis (27)	
	Wave-length Å	Sensi-tivity ppm	Detec-tion limit ppm	Wave-length Å	Sensi-tivity ppm	Detec-tion limit ppm	Wave-length Å	Sensi-tivity ppm
La	3,928	80	80	5,501	100	20	3,574	100
	5,501	42	8				3,928	280
Ce	no data			no data			no data	
Pr	4,914	20		4,940	150	20	4,951	72
	4,951	13	10					
Nd	4,634	10	2	4,925	35	1	5,133	92
							4,634	35
							4,897	48
Pm	no data			no data			no data	
Sm	4,297	15	5	5,175	30	1	4,297	21
	5,200	15					4,760	29
Eu	4,584	3	0·2	no data			4,594	1·8
	4,627	4					4,627	3·0
	4,661	4					4,661	3·0
Gd	3,684	30	4	3,684	90	15	3,684	38
	4,078	30					4,078	42
Tb	4,326	7·5	2	4,326	20	5	no data	
Dy	4,212	1·5	0·2	4,046	2	0·1	4,212	1·5
	4,046	1·8						
Ho	4,104	2·5	0·5	4,104	2	0·5	4,104	2·2
	4,053	3						
Er	4,008	1·5	0·2	4,008	2	0·1	4,008	1·4
	4,151	2						
Tm	no data			4,094	3	5	no data	
Yb	3,988	0·2	0·04	3,988	0·5	0·01	3,988	0·25
Lu	no data			3,282	80	50	3,360	12
							3,312	21

up to about 6 or 7 eV must be considered (223). Thus, the group of elements which may be influenced by the ionization equilibria in the flame includes Al, Sc, Y, the rare earths, Zr, Hf, V, Nb, and the actinides (besides the alkali metals and alkaline earths). To suppress ionization, alkali halides are added in excess to the sprayed solution.

An enhancing effect of hydrofluoric acid on the determination of Zr, Ti, Hf and Ta contents (27) and of hydrochloric acid on zirconium (313A) has been reported. This enhancement is probably connected with the evaporation rate of the solid particles. On the other hand, it has been found that hydrochloric acid lowers the aluminium absorption (27, 218), as also do high concentrations of iron $(10,000 \text{ ppm}) - (27)$. Low concentrations of some cations (Zn, Ca, Cu) enhance the absorption by some 10% (218).

High brightness lamps were explored for silicon, titanium and vanadium and the sensitivity of various lines were compared (69A). Vanadium has also been determined in steels (67), after dissolving the samples in a mixture of sulphuric and phosphoric acids and adding nitric acid dropwise. When the influence of the acids on the sample intake rate was corrected it was found that sulphuric acid had a depressive effect, whereas phosphoric acid had an enhancing effect. According to the authors this enhancing effect may probably be ascribed to the fact that phosphoric acid prevents the reduction of vanadium pentoxide to the trioxide which has a much lower vapour pressure (67). Vanadium in oils was determined after tenfold dilution with xylene using an addition method (67).

The nitrous oxide-acetylene flame was also investigated for use in the measurement of rare earths concentrations. The rare earths were extracted by a 10% solution of di-2-ethylhexyl phosphoric acid in MIBK. Y, Dy, Ho, Er, Yb, Tm, and Lu are most efficiently extracted at a pH of 1, Nd, Sm, Tb and Eu at a pH of 2, Gd at a pH of 3·5 and La and Pr at a pH of 4 (28). Absorbance values for different rare earth lines (namely Sm, Eu, Tb, Ho, Er, Dy, Gd, La, Pr and Yb) are also tabulated (223A). Lines for W, U, Sc and Zr are also given.

Prior to the introduction of the nitrous oxide-acetylene flame, experiments with reducing oxy-acetylene flames and total consumption burners were performed. It has been generally observed that the sensitivity depends considerably on the localization of the light beam in the flame. Concentrations of aluminium has been determined (71, 237). However, absorption spectra of Be, Al, V, Ti (307), V, Nb, Ti, Mo, W, Re (188), V, Ti, Nb, Sc, Y, Re (109), the rare earths (244), Eu, Tm, Yb (306) and Pr (387) have only been explored, but were not exploited for analytical work. The most sensitive lines reported of these elements are included in Table 9.13 at the end of this book.

Some of these "refractory" element concentrations have been measured using hollow cathode absorption sources. Similarly aluminium and steel were analysed for silicon concentrations, using a sputtering chamber (352). The isotopic analysis of uranium was successfully accomplished (138), whereas for boron the isotope shift was found to be too small (139) and no difference of the two isotopes B^{10} and B^{11} was observed. Lvov's graphite furnace was applied to the estimation of aluminium in water, and in acids and, alloys (253). The absolute sensitivity in these was 1.5×10^{-11} gm, giving a relative sensitivity in alloys of $5 \times 10^{-5}\%$.

9.9 ATOMIC FLUORESCENCE SPECTROMETRY

The possibility of using atomic fluorescence as an analytical method has already been mentioned in Chapter 3. Here, some details of the choice of analytical conditions and the sensitivities achieved, will be given.

A block diagram of an atomic fluorescence spectrometer is given in Fig. 9.2. An important condition for the successful application is a low level of scattered light other than the fluorescent light. The flame is, therefore, usually placed in a baffle box with light traps. Compared with atomic absorption, atomic fluorescence has two main advantages. Firstly because fluorescent radiation is observed in a direction perpendicular to the incident exciting light beam, the use of continuous sources is possible. A single source may be used for different elements and therefore the way to a rapid sequential elemental analysis is opened. The second advantage is the possibility of further improving sensitivity by improving the emissive power of the light sources. So far results (lowest detection limits) have been achieved with vapour discharge lamps and microwave electrodeless discharge tubes. The detection limits with continuous sources (e.g. high pressure xenon lamps) are poor because of the high level of scattered light (see Table 9.12).

Some of the atoms excited by the absorption of radiation lose their energy by collisions of the second kind. The signal due to the fluorescent light is, therefore, small and may easily become lost in the observed noise. This noise consists of scattered light from the source which, if the source

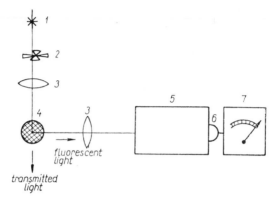

Fig. 9.2. Schematic arrangement for carrying out atomic fluorescence spectrometry
1 — light source, 2 — chopper, 3 — lenses, 4 — flame, 5 — monochromator, 6 —
detector, 7 — amplifier and readout system

was modulated, is in phase with the fluorescent radiation and is therefore simultaneously amplified and measured. According to the results so far published, the scattered light intensity seems to be smaller with pre-mixed flames than with total consumption burners (79).

A second contribution to the noise are all the in-phase fluctuations of the flame background emission. The smaller the emitted background, the smaller also its contribution to the noise. Background radiation depends mainly on the flame used. Acetylene seems to be much less suitable than hydrogen or propane (79).

Air pre-mixed flames or oxygen with total consumption burners are most often used. In some cases enhancement of the fluorescence signal was achieved by using a mixture of oxygen and argon instead of pure oxygen (345), or by spraying the sample with hydrogen combusted only with entrained air (102).

Table 9.12

REVIEW OF DETECTION LIMITS ATTAINED BY ATOMIC FLUORESCENCE
SPECTROMETRY

Flame and burner	Light source	Detection limit ppm		Reference
O_2–H_2 O_2–C_2H_2 Beckman	vapour discharge lamps	Zn Cd Hg	0·04 0·1 0·5	376
O_2–H_2 O_2–C_2H_2 Beckman	vapour discharge lamps electrodeless discharge tubes	Zn Cd Hg Tl	0·04 0·1 0·1 1·0	377
O_2–H_2 Beckman	vapour discharge lamps	Zn Cd Tl Hg In	0·0001 0·0002 0·04 0·1 10	226
O_2–H_2 O_2–Ar–H_2 Beckman	high pressure xenon lamps	Ag Au Ba Bi Ca Cd Cu Ga Mg Ni Pb Tl Zn	0·08 3·5 7 2 1·5 0·08 0·35 20 0·2 13 7·5 0·55 0·6	345
C_2H_2-air– Mékèr	vapour discharge lamps	Cd	0·002	78
H_2-air propane-air Mékèr	high pressure xenon lamps	Ag Cd Co	0·1 0·25 1·0	79

Table 9.12 continued

Flame and burner	Light source	Detection limit ppm		Reference
		Cu	0·4	
		Fe	5·0	
		Mg	2·0	
		Mn	0·15	
		Pb	10	
		Tl	0·5	
		Zn	0·6	
H_2-entrained air Beckman	high pressure xenon lamps	Ag	0·001	102
		Co	0·5	
		Mg	0·01	
		Zn	0·03	

Originally it had been expected that fluorescent radiation would be susceptible to interferences due to the dependence of the quantum efficiency coefficient* on the composition of the flame gases. It seems, however, that this fear was unnecessary and that atomic fluorescence is as free from inter-element effects as atomic absorption spectrometry (141).

By optimization of all the experimental parameters detection limits achieved may be several orders of magnitude better than the atomic absorption method (see Table 9.13). However, so far the flame used as a fluorescent medium only ensures evaporation and atomization of the samples for a limited number of elements. Further developments depend primarily on improvements in the methods of preparation of such media.

---

* In this context the quantum efficiency is the ratio of the number of incident photons absorbed by the atoms to the emitted in the resonance fluorescence process. This, as would be expected, depends on the number of collisions of the second kind, etc., taking place in the flame.

Table 9.13

LINES USED IN ATOMIC ABSORPTION SPECTROSCOPY

D — dissociation energy of the oxide in eV; E_i — ionization energy; f — oscillator strength. Lines corresponding to transitions from other than ground states are marked with an asterisk. Qualitative indication of the sensitivity: VS — very strong, S — strong, M — medium, W — weak

Element	Wavelength nm	Oscillator strength	Sensitivity in ppm		
			C_2H_2–air laminar	C_2H_2–O_2 total consumption burner	C_2H_2–N_2O laminar
Ag $D = 1\cdot4$ $E_i = 7\cdot57$	328·07 338·29	0·51 0·25	0·1 0·15		
Al $D = 5\cdot0$ $E_i = 5\cdot98$	308·22 309·28 ⎫ 309·27* ⎭ 394·40 396·15*	0·22 0·23 0·15 0·15			3 1 4·2 2·5
As $D = 4\cdot9$ $E_i = 9\cdot81$	189·0 193·70 197·20	0·095 0·07	1 2 3		
Au $E_i = 9\cdot22$	242·80 267·60	0·3 0·19	0·5 2·0		
B $D = 7\cdot95$ $E_i = 8\cdot29$	249·68 249·77*	0·32 0·33	250		100 50
Ba $D = 5\cdot95$ $E_i = 5\cdot21$	553·56	1·40	5		0·4

Table 9.13 continued 1

Element	Wavelength nm	Oscillator strength	Sensitivity in ppm		
			C_2H_2–air laminar	C_2H_2–O_2 total consumption burner	C_2H_2–N_2O laminar
Be $D = 4·6$ $E_i = 9·32$	234·86	0·24	0·2		0·03
Bi $D = 4·0$ $E_i = 7·29$	206·17 222·83 223·06 306·77	0·095 0·0025 0·012 0·25	1 4 1 1		
Ca $D = 5·0$ $E_i = 6·11$	422·67 239·86	1·49 0·037	0·1 20·0		0·03
Cd $D = 3·8$ $E_i = 8·99$	228·8 326·11	1·2 0·0018	0·03 20		
Co $E_i = 7·86$	240·72 241·16* 242·49 243·22* 252·14 304·40 345·35* 352·68	0·22 0·34 0·19 0·27 0·19 0·04 0·60; 0·46 0·048	0·2 0·7 0·3 0·9 0·5 2·6 4 3		
Cr $D = 4·2$ $E_i = 6·76$	357·87 359·35 360·53 425·43	0·34 0·27 0·19 0·10	0·15 0·20 0·5		

Table 9.13 continued II

Element	Wavelength nm	Oscillator strength	Sensitivity in ppm		
			C_2H_2–air laminar	C_2H_2–O_2 total consumption burner	C_2H_2–N_2O laminar
Cs	455·54		20		
$E_i = 3·87$	852·11	0·80	0·5		
	894·35	0·40			
Cu	216·51	0·009	0·68		
$D = 4·9$	217·89	0·011	0·44		
$E_i = 7·72$	218·17	0·008	0·88		
	222·57	0·0039	2		
	222·78*	0·08	2		
	324·75	0·74; 0·32	0·1		
	327·40	0·38; 0·15	0·2		
Dy	404·60				1·8
$E_i = 6·2$	419·49			VS	3·4
	421·17				1·5
Er	381·03			S	
$E_i = 6·2$	400·79			VS	1·4
	415·11			VS	2·0
Eu	311·14	0·18		S	44
$E_i = 5·64$	321·06	0·07		S	35
	321·28	0·17		S	40
	333·43	0·12		S (236)	55
	459·40	0·22		VS 2·5	2·8–0·8
	462·72	0·20		VS 3	3·7
	466·19	0·17		VS 3·6	4·3
Fe	248·33	0·34	0·15		
$D = 4·0$	248·81*	0·45	0·2		
$E_i = 7·87$	252·29	0·30	0·2		
	252·74*	0·21	0·6		
	271·90	0·15	0·4		

Table 9.13 continued III

Element	Wavelength nm	Oscillator strength	Sensitivity in ppm		
			C_2H_2–air laminar	C_2H_2–O_2 total consumption burner	C_2H_2–N_2O laminar
	272·09*	0·1	0·9		
	296·69	0·056	1·2		
	302·06	0·083	0·5		
	344·06	0·055	2·8		
	371·99	0·036; 0·057	1·0		
	385·99	0·034	2·0		
Ga	287·42	0·32	2·3		
$D = 2·5$	294·36*	0·290⎱	2·4		
$E_i = 6·00$	294·42*	0·038⎰			
	403·30	0·13	6·2		
	417·21*	0·14	3·7		
Gd	368·41			W	38
$D = 6·0$	378·31				46
$E_i = 6·16$	407·87				42
Ge	259·25*	0·37	12		15
$D = 6·5$	265·16	0·84	5		2·5
$E_i = 7·88$	269·13*	0·27	13		40
	270·96*	0·43	12		22
	275·46*	0·22	10		20
Hf	307·29	0·09			14 .
$E_i = 6·8$					
Hg	184·96	1·2			
$E_i = 10·43$	253·65	0·03	10		
Ho	405·39			VS	2·8
	410·38			VS	2·2
	416·30			VS	3·5
	425·44			VS	85

Table 9.13 continued IV

Element	Wavelength nm	Oscillator strength	Sensitivity in ppm		
			C_2H_2-air laminar	$C_2H_2-O_2$ total con- sumption burner	$C_2H_2-N_2O$ laminar
In	256·02	0·23	11		
$D = 1·1$	303·94	0·36; 0·45	0·9		
$E_i = 5·78$	325·61*	0·37 ⎫			
	325·86*	0·06 ⎭	0·9		
	410·48	0·14	2·6		
	451·13*	0·16	2·8		
Ir	263·97	0·059	44		
$E_i = 9$	266·48	0·065	67		
	284·97	0·056	34		
	292·48	0·053	54		
K	404·41	0·11	5		
$E_i = 4·34$	766·49	0·69 ⎫			
	769·89	0·34 ⎭	0·1		
La	357·44	0·12		M	110
$D = 7·0$	392·76	0·18			280
$E_i = 5·61$	550·13	0·15			50
Li	323·26	0·026	15		
$E_i = 5·39$	670·78	0·71	0·07		
Lu	308·15*	0·096		S	
$D = 4·3$	328·17*	0·086			80
$E_i = 6·15$	335·96*	0·076			12
Mg	II. 279·55	1·65	5		
$D = 4·3$	285·21	1·2	0·01		
$E_i = 7·64$					
Mn	210·96		1		
$D = 4$	222·18	0·11	1		
$E_i = 7·43$	279·48	0·58	0·05		

Table 9.13 continued V

Element	Wavelength nm	Oscillator strength	Sensitivity in ppm		
			C_2H_2–air laminar	C_2H_2–O_2 total consumption burner	C_2H_2–N_2O laminar
	279·83	0·42	0·08		
	280·11	0·29	0·12		
	403·07	0·056 ⎫			
	403·31	0·040 ⎬ 1·0			
	403·45	0·027 ⎭			
Mo	313·26	0·20	1·0		0·4
$E_i = 7·10$	317·04	0·12			
	379·83	0·13	1·5	0·03	
Na	330·23	0·055	5·0		
$E_i = 5·14$	588·99	0·76 ⎱			
	589·69	0·39 ⎰ 0·05			
Nb	334·91*	0·085			40
$D = 4·0$	358·03	0·12			30
$E_i = 6·88$	405·89*	0·19		250	35
	407·97*	0·15		250	30
	410·09*	0·11		250	
Nd	463·43	0·08		M	10
$E_i = 5·45$	492·45	0·09		S	40
Ni	231·09	0·066	0·4		
$E_i = 7·61$	232·00	0·095	0·2		
	234·55	0·051	2		
	300·25*	0·13	6		
	305·08*	0·10	3·5		
	341·48*	0·30; 0·14	3·0		
	346·17*	0·16; 0·08	6		
	352·45*	0·12	2·5		
Os	290·9		3		1
$E_i = 8·73$	305·9		5		2

Table 9.13 continued VI

Element	Wavelength nm	Oscillator strength	Sensitivity in ppm C_2H_2–air laminar	C_2H_2–O_2 total consumption burner	C_2H_2–N_2O laminar
P $E_i = 10.48$	177·48				
Pb $D = 4.1$ $E_i = 7.42$	217·00 261·42* 283·31	0·39 0·4 0·21	0·5 50 1·0		
Pd $E_i = 8.33$	244·79 247·64 276·31 340·46*	0·074 0·1 0·071 0·29	1 i 3 1·5		
Pr $E_i = 5.57$	495·14 504·55 513·34			M M M	13 42 23
Pt $E_i = 9.0$	217·47 265·94	0·12	2·7		
Rb $E_i = 4.18$	420·19 780·02 794·76	0·80 0·40	10 0·2		
Re $E_i = 7.87$	345·19 346·05 346·47	0·06 0·2 0·13	25	50 25 25	33 12 20
Rh $E_i = 7.45$	343·49 369·24	0·073 0·058	0·3 0·6		
Ru $E_i = 7.34$	349·89 372·80 379·93	0·10 0·087 0·056	2		

Table 9.13 continued VII

| Element | Wavelength nm | Oscillator strength | Sensitivity in ppm | | |
			C_2H_2–air laminar	C_2H_2–O_2 total consumption burner	C_2H_2–N_2O laminar
Sb	206·84	0·1	1		
$D = 3·2$	217·59	0·045	1		
$E_i = 8·64$	231·15	0·03	1·5		
Sc	326·99	0·37		10	2·8
$D = 6·0$	327·36*	0·31		10	2·0
$E_i = 6·54$	390·75	0·67		5	1·1
	391·18*	0·55		5	0·8
	402·04	0·60		5	1·7
	402·37*	0·41		5	1·2
Se	196·1	0·12	2		
$D = 3·5$	203·99*	0·26			
$E_i = 9·75$	206·28*	0·30			
Si	250·69*	0·2			3·1
	251·43	0·54			3·8
$E_i = 8·15$	251·61*	0·26	15	5	1·2
Sm	380·39			M	
	399·00			M	
$E_i = 5·6$	429·67*				20
	520·06*				30
Sn	224·61	0·41	1 †		2·3
$D = 5·7$	235·48*	0·27	1·6		2·4
$E_i = 7·34$	254·66	0·07			
	286·33	0·23	1·3		3·6
Sr	II. 407·77	0·76	3·5		
$D = 4·85$	460·73	1·54	0·2		0·06
$E_i = 5·69$					

† The sensitivity for tin was found in a hydrogen-air flame (68)

Table 9.13 continued VIII

Element	Wavelength nm	Oscillator strength	Sensitivity in ppm		
			C_2H_2–air laminar	C_2H_2–O_2 total consumption burner	C_2H_2–N_2O laminar
Ta $E_i = 7.88$	271.47	0.055			30
Tb	431.88			S	9
	432.65			S	7.5
	433.84			S	15
Te $D = 2.7$ $E_i = 9.01$	214.28	0.08	1.5		
Th $D = 8.6$ $E_i = 6.2$					
Ti	319.99*	0.23			2.0
	337.15	0.20			2.0
$D = 6.9$	363.55	0.24		16	5.6
$E_i = 6.82$	364.27*	0.25		12	1.8
	365.35*	0.22		12	1.6
	399.86*	0.031; 0.18		16	4.3
Tl	237.97	0.07			
	276.79	0.27; 0.23	0.8		
$E_i = 6.11$	377.57	0.13; 0.11			
Tm	388.31	0.14		VS	
$E_i = 6.2$	388.73	0.11		VS	
	409.42	0.16		35	3
	410.58	0.15		38	
	418.76	0.12		67	
	420.37	0.09		85	

Table 9.13 continued IX

Element	Wavelength nm	Oscillator strength	Sensitivity in ppm		
			C_2H_2–air laminar	C_2H_2–O_2 total con- sumption burner	C_2H_2–N_2O laminar
U	351·46				200
	358·49				120
$E_i = 6·2$					
V	306·64*				0·5
	318·34*	0·5	25⎫		1·3
$D = 5·5$	318·39*	0·66	10⎭		
$E_i = 6·74$	318·54*	0·40	25		1·0
	370·36*				0·5
	385·58*	0·98	50		2
	437·92*	0·20; 0·30	50		4·0
W	255·14	0·8			5·3
$E_i = 7·98$	294·70*	0·98			18
	400·88*				25
Y	407·74	0·27	50		2·0
$D = 7$	410·24*	0·21	100		1·5
$E_i = 6·51$	412·83*	0·18	100		2·0
	414·29	0·20	100		3·5
Yb	246·45	0·24	VS		1·6
	346·44	0·13	VS		0·8
$E_i = 6·22$	398·80	0·38	10		0·25
Zn	213·96	1·2		0·04	
$D = 4$					
$E_i = 9·39$	307·59	0·00017		150	
Zr	360·12*	0·22			15
$D = 7·8$					
$E_i = 6·84$					

RECENTLY PUBLISHED PAPERS

In this paragraph papers which have appeared after finishing the manuscript of this book will be dealt with and some recent trends in atomic absorption and atomic fluorescence spectrometry shortly mentioned.

As might have been expected, a number of refractory elements have been determined with the nitrous oxide-acetylene flame. These comprise Al and Be (424), Ti (407), V (425), B, Be, Ge and Nb (415) as well as some of the rare earths (410, 409). KIRKBRIGHT, PETERS and WEST (411) studying the $N_2O-C_2H_2$ flame found close correlation between the emission of CN bands and the spectral lines of refractory elements, which extended throughout the "red feather" zone. The effectiveness in atomizing refractory oxides is, according to their conclusions, only partially due to the high temperature of this flame but mostly due to the extremely low concentration of oxygen in the red feather, which actually is a second reaction zone with high CN and NH concentrations where combustion reactions with probably NO and OH particles are proceeding and which is shielded from the atmosphere by the outer diffusion cone.

Several analytical papers dealing with less frequently measured elements have also appeared. These include antimony (423), bismuth (417), rhenium (428), thallium (432). Arsenic has been determined with a graphite tube in an argon chamber (420). The construction according to MASSMANN (420) is somewhat simpler and easier to use than that of LVOV. The detection limits are, however, higher (419). Next to these Zn and Cd have been determined in silicate rocks (430), chromium in biological materials (403) and lead in gasoline either directly (434) or after separation by gas chromatography (413).

Enrichment of the solution measured by extraction has been quite frequently applied for trace elements. BURRELL used extraction for the determination of Co, Ni, Fe, and Mn in marine waters (400) and BROOKS, PRESLEY and KAPLAN (399) investigated the possibilities of the APDC-MIBK system for different elements. A review on extraction systems used in flame photometry is given by ZOLOTOV and KUZMIN (437).

The sensitivity enhancement by organic solvents in flame photometry has also been studied (426). The use of a T-shaped flame adapter applied formerly for the determination of Cd, Cu and Zn (272A) has been extended also for Mn, Fe, Co and Ni (427). Absorption tubes have been used for the determination of Cd and Zn (436). THILLIEZ (431) used a special burner with an absorption tube for the determination of lead in atmospheric air.

The precision of atomic absorption routine analyses has been also a matter of interest and is discussed in several papers (433, 422). Comparing the precision when using photoelectric and photographic detection IVANOV and TALALAEV (408) found the latter several times inferior. LANG suggested a possible way to eliminating flame noise (414).

The performance of continuous sources in atomic absorption spectro-photometry has been theoretically investigated by DE GALAN, MCGEE and WINEFORDNER (405). Among the possible continuous sources the xenon arc lamp offers best results and it has been experimentally tried with a total consumption burner (404) as well as with an absorption tube (421).

On the instrumental side hollow cathode lamps with shielded cathodes bring a definite improvement (416). By shielding the outer side of the cathode the discharge is limited to the cavity and the intensity of light emitted increases.

REFERENCES

Monographs

1. BAIR E. J.: *Introduction to Chemical Instrumentation*, McGraw-Hill, New York (1962).
2. CORLISS CH. H., BOZMAN W. R.: *Experimental Transition Probabilities for Spectral Lines of Seventy Elements*, Nat. Bur. Stand. Monograph 53, Washington (1962).
3. DEAN J. A.: *Flame Photometry*, McGraw-Hill Book Com. Inc., New York (1960).
4. ELWELL W. T., GIDLEY J. A. F.: *Atomic Absorption Spectrophotometry*, Pergamon Press, London (1961).
5. FRISH S. E.: *Opticheskyje spektri atomov*, Gos. izdat. fiz.-mat. lit., Moskva (1963).
6. GAYDON A. G.: *The Spectroscopy of Flames*, Chapman and Hall Ltd., London (1957).
7. HERRMANN R., ALKEMADE C. TH. J.: *Flammenphotometrie*, Springer Vrlg. Berlin, Göttingen, Heidelberg (1960).
8. IVANOV N. P.: *Atomno-absorbcionnyj analiz*, IREA, Moskva (1965).
9. LVOV B. V.: *Atomno-absorbcionnyj spektralnyj analiz*, Izdatelstvo "Nauka", Moskva (1966).
9A. MAVRODINEAU R., BOITEUX H.: *Flame spectroscopy*, John Wiley and Sons, New York (1965).
10. MITCHELL A. C., ZEMANSKY M. W.: *Resonance Radiation and Excited Atoms*, Cambridge Univ. Press (1961).
11. ROBINSON J. W.: *Atomic Absorption Spectroscopy*, Marcel Dekker Inc., New York (1966).
11A. ANGINO E. E. BILLINGS G. K.: *Atomic Absorption Spectrophotometry in Geology*, Elsevier (1968).
11B. RAMÍREZ-MUÑOZ J.: *Atomic-Absorption Spectroscopy*, Elsevier (1968).

Papers

(abbreviation AAN stands for Atomic Absorption Newsletter, Perkin-Elmer Corp.)

12. ADAMS P. B., PASSMORE W. O.: *Anal. Chem.* **38**, 630 (1966).
13. AGAZZI E. J.: *Anal. Chem.* **37**, 365 (1965).
14. ALKEMADE C. T. J., MILATZ J. M. W.: *J. Opt. Soc. Am.* **45**, 583 (1955); *Appl. Sci. Res.* **43**, 289 (1955).
15. ALKEMADE C. T. J., VOORHUIS M. H.: *Z. anal. Chem.* **163**, 91 (1958).
16. ALKEMADE C. T. J.: *Coll. Spec. Int.* X, College Park, Maryland (1962).
16A. ALKEMADE C. T. J.: *Anal. Chem.* **38**, 1252 (1966).
17. ALLAN J. E.: *Analyst* **83**, 466 (1958).
18. ALLAN J. E.: *Spectrochim. Acta* **15**, 800 (1959).
19. ALLAN J. E.: *Nature* **187**, 1110 (1960).
20. ALLAN J. E.: *Spectrochim. Acta* **17**, 459 (1961).
21. ALLAN J. E.: *Spectrochim. Acta* **17**, 467 (1961).
22. ALLAN J. E.: *Analyst* **86**, 530 (1961).
23. ALLAN J. E.: *Spectrochim. Acta* **18**, 259 (1962).
24. ALLAN J. E.: *Spectrochim. Acta* **18**, 605 (1962).
25. AMOS M. D., THOMAS P. E.: *Anal. chim. Acta* **32**, 139 (1965).
26. AMOS M. D.: Personal communication.
27. AMOS M. D., WILLIS J. B.: *Spectrochim. Acta* **22**, 1325 (1966).
28. ANDERSON J. W.: 5th Natl. Meeting, S. A. S., Chicago (1966).
29. ANDREW T. R., NICHOLS P. N. R.: *Analyst* **87**, 25 (1962).
30. ANGINO E. E., BILLINGS G. K.: *Geochim. Cosmochim. Acta* **30**, 153 (1966).
31. BAKER C. A., GARTON F. W. J.: *UKAEA, A. E. R. E.* R 3490 (1961).
32. BARNES L.: *Anal. Chem.* **38**, 1083 (1966).
33. BELCHER C. B., BOZAY H. M.: *Anal. Chim. Acta* **26**, 322 (1962).
34. BELCHER C. B., BROOKS K. A.: *Anal. Chim. Acta* **29**, 202 (1963).
35. BELCHER C. B.: *Anal. Chim. Acta* **29**, 340 (1963).
36. BELCHER C. B., KINSON K.: *Anal. Chim. Acta* **30**, 483 (1964).
37. BELCHER R., DAGNALL R. M., WEST T. S.: *Talanta* **11**, 1257 (1964).
37A. BELL G. F.: *AAN* **5**, 73 (1966).
38. BELL W. E., BLOOM A. L., LYNCH J.: *Rev. Sci. Instrum.* **32**, 688 (1961).
39. BELT CH. B.: *Economic Geology* **59**, 240 (1964).
40. BERMAN E.: *AAN* **3**, 111 (1964).
41. BERMAN E.: *AAN* **4**, 296 (1965).
42. BERRY W. L., JOHNSON C. H.: *Appl. Spectrosc.* **20**, 209 (1966).
43. BEYER M.: *AAN* **4**, 212 (1965).
44. BILLINGS G. K., ADAMS J. A. S.: *AAN* **23**, 1 (1964).
45. BILLINGS G. K.: *AAN* **4**, 312 (1965).
46. BILLINGS G. K.: *AAN* **4**, 357 (1965).
47. BILLINGS G. K., ANGINO E. E.: *Bull. Canadian Petroleum Geol.* **13**, 529 (1965).

48. BILLINGS G. K.: *Bull. Canadian Petroleum Geol.* **13**, 532 (1965).
49. BODRECOVA A. I., LVOV B. V., PAVLOVSKAJA E. N., PROKOFJEV V. K.: *Zh. prikl. spektroskopii* **2**, 97 (1965).
50. BOLING E. A.: *Anal. Chem.* **37**, 482 (1965).
51. BOLING E. A.: *Spectrochim. Acta* **22**, 425 (1966).
52. BORDONALI C., BIANCIFIORI M. A., BESAZZA G.: *Chim. Ind.* (Milan) **47**, 397 (1965).
53. BOWMAN J. A., SULLIVAN J. V., WALSH A.: *Spectrochim. Acta* **22**, 205 (1966).
54. BOX G. F., WALSH A.: *Spectrochim. Acta* **16**, 255 (1960).
55. BUCHANAN J. R., MURAOKA T. T.: *AAN* **24**, 1 (1964).
56. BURRELL D. C.: *AAN* **4**, 309 (1965).
57. BURRELL D. C.: *AAN* **4**, 328 (1965).
58. BURROWS J. A., HEERDT J. C., WILLIS J. B.: *Anal. Chem.* **37**, 579 (1965).
59. BUTLER L. R. P.: *S. Afr. Ind. Chemist* **15**, 162 (1961).
60. BUTLER L. R. P.: *J. S. Afr. Inst. Min. Metall.* **62**, 780 (1962).
61. BUTLER L. R. P.: *J. S. Afr. Inst. Min. Metall.* **62**, 786 (1962).
62. BUTLER L. R. P., BRINK D.: *S. Afr. Ind. Chemist* **17**, 152 (1963).
63. BUTLER L. R. P., STRASHEIM A., STRELOW F. W. E., MATHEWS P., FEAST E. C.: *Coll. Spec. Int.* **XII.** Exeter (1965).
64. BUTLER L. R. P., STRASHEIM A.: *Spectrochim. Acta* **21**, 1207 (1960).
65. BUTLER L. R. P., MATHEWS P. M.: *Anal. Chim. Acta* **36**, 319 (1966).
66. CAPACHO-DELGADO L., SPRAGUE S.: *AAN* **4**, 363 (1965).
67. CAPACHO-DELGADO L., MANNING D. C.: *AAN* **5**, 1 (1966).
68. CAPACHO-DELGADO L., MANNING D. C.: *Spectrochim. Acta* **22**, 1505 (1966).
69. CARTWRIGHT J. S., SEBENS C., SLAVIN W.: *AAN* **5**, 22 (1966).
69A. CARTWRIGHT J. S., SEBENS C., MANNING D. C.: *AAN* **5**, 91 (1966).
70. CELLIER K. M., STACE H. C. T.: *Appl. Spectrosc.* **20**, 26 (1966).
71. CHAKRABARTI CH. L., LYLES G. R., DOWLING F. B.: *Anal. Chim. Acta* **24**, 489 (1963).
72. CHAKRABARTI CH. L., ROBINSON J. W., WEST P. W.: *Anal. Chim. Acta* **34**, 269 (1966).
73. CHANG T. L., GOVER T. A., HARRISON W. W.: *Anal. Chim. Acta* **34**, 17 (1966).
74. CLINTON O. E.: *Spectrochim. Acta* **16**, 985 (1960).
75. CROSSWHITE H. M., DIEKE G. H., LEGAGNEUR C. S.: *J. Opt. Soc. Am.* **45**, 270 (1955).
76. DAGNALL R. M., WEST T. S.: *Talanta* **11**, 1553 (1964).
77. DAGNALL R. M., WEST T. S., YOUNG P.: *Anal. Chem.* **38** 358 (1966).
78. DAGNALL R. M., WEST T. S., YOUNG P.: *Talanta* **13**, 803 (1966).
79. DAGNALL R. M., THOMPSON K. C., WEST T. S.: *Anal. Chim. Acta* **38**, 269 (1966).
80. DAVEY B. G.: *Spectrochim. Acta* **19**, 1319 (1963).
81. DAVID D. J.: *Analyst* **83**, 655 (1958).
82. DAVID D. J.: *Analyst* **84**, 536 (1959).

83. DAVID D. J.: *Nature* **187**, 1109 (1960).
84. DAVID D. J.: *Analyst* **85**, 495 (1960).
85. DAVID D. J.: *Analyst* **85**, 779 (1960).
86. DAVID D. J.: *Analyst* **86**, 730 (1961).
87. DAVID D. J.: *Analyst* **87**, 576 (1962).
88. DAVID D. J.: *AAN* **9** (1962).
89. DAVID D. J.: *Spectrochim. Acta* **20**, 1185 (1964).
90. DAVIES D. A., VENN R., WILLIS J. B.: *J. Sci. Instrum.* **42**, 816 (1965).
91. DAWSON J. B., HEATON F. W.: *Biochem. J.* **80**, 99 (1961).
92. DAWSON J. B., ELLIS D. J.: *Coll. Spec. Int.* **XII.** Exeter (1965).
93. DEAN J. A., CARNES W. J.: *Anal. Chem.* **34**, 192 (1962).
94. DELAUGHTER B.: *AAN* **4**, 273 (1965).
95. DICKSON R. E., JOHNSON C. M.: *Appl. Spectrosc.* **20**, 214 (1966).
96. DINNIN J. I.: *Anal. Chem.* **32**, 1475 (1960).
97. DUNKEN H., PFORR G., MIKKELEIT W., GELLER K.: *Spectrochim. Acta* **20**, 1531 (1964).
98. DVOŘÁK J., RUBEŠKA I.: *Chem. listy* **57**, 561 (1963).
99. DYCK R.: *AAN* **4**, 170 (1965).
100. EISEN J.: *Z. Erzbergbau Metallhüttenwes.* **16**, 579 (1963).
101. ELENBAAS W.: *Philips Tech. Rev.* **11**, 299 (1950).
102. ELLIS D. W., DEMERS D. R.: *Anal. Chem.* **38**, 1943 (1966).
103. ELWELL W. T., GIDLEY J. A. F.: *Anal. Chim. Acta* **24**, 71 (1961).
104. ELWELL W. T., GIDLEY J. A. F.: *Anal. Chem.*, Proc. Int. Sympos. Birmingham Univ. **1962**, 291 (1963).
105. ERDEY L., SVEHLA G., KOLTAI L.: *Talanta* **10**, 531 (1963).
106. ERING G., MAGEE R. J.: *Anal. Chim. Acta* **31**, 197 (1964).
107. FABRICAND B. P., SAWYER R. R., UNGAR S. G., ADLER S.: *Geochim. et Cosmochim. Acta* **26**, 1023 (1962).
108. FARRAR B.: *AAN* **4**, 325 (1965).
109. FASSEL V. A., MOSSOTTI V. G.: *Anal. Chem.* **35**, 252 (1963).
110. FASSEL V. A., MOSSOTTI V. G.: GROSSMAN W. E. L., KNISELEY R. N.: *Coll. Spec. Int.* **XII.** Exeter (1965).
111. FASSEL V. A., MOSSOTTI V. G., GROSSMAN W. E. L., KNISELEY R. N.: *Spectrochim. Acta* **22**, 347 (1966).
112. FELDMAN F. J., PURDY W. C.: *Anal. Chim. Acta* **33**, 273 (1965).
113. FINKELSTEIN N. P., JANSEN A. V.: *S. Afr. Ind. Chemists* **15**, 106 (1961).
114. FIRMAN R. J.: *Spectrochim. Acta* **21**, 341 (1965).
115. FELDMAN C., DHUMWAD R. K.: U. S. At. Energy Comm. *TID* 7655, 379 (1962).
116. FRANK C. W., SCHRENK W. G., MELOAN C. E.: *Anal. Chem.* **38**, 1005 (1966).
117. FREY S. W.: *AAN* **3**, 127 (1964).
118. FRIED K. E., DIEFENDERFER A. J.: *Anal. Chem.* **38**, 1763 (1966).
119. FUKUSHIMA S.: *Mikrochim. Acta* **1960**, 332.
120. FUWA KEIICHIRO, VALLEE B. L.: *Anal. Chem.* **35**, 942 (1963).

121. FUWA K., PULIDO P., MCKAY R., VALLEE B. L.: *Anal. Chem.* **36**, 2407 (1964).
122. DE GALAN L., WINEFORDNER J. D.: *Anal. Chem.* **38**, 1412 (1966).
123. GATEHOUSE B. M., WALSH A.: *Spectrochim. Acta* **16**, 602 (1960).
124. GATEHOUSE B. M., WILLIS J. B.: *Spectrochim. Acta* **17**, 710 (1961).
125. GAUMER M. W., SPRAGUE S., SLAVIN W.: *AAN* **5**, 58 (1966).
126. GERBATSCH R.: *Emissionsspektroskopie*, Akad. Verlag, Berlin (1964), p. 181.
127. GIBSON J. H., GROSSMANN W. E. L., COOKE W. D.: *Anal. Chem.*, Proc. Feigl Anniversary Sympos., Birmingham Univ. 1962, Elsevier.
128. GIBSON J. H., GROSSMAN E. L., COOKE W. D.: *Anal. Chem.* **35**, 266 (1963).
129. GIDLEY J. A. F., JONES J. T.: *Analyst* **85**, 249 (1960).
130. GIDLEY J. A. F.: *Limitations of Detection in Spectrochemical Analysis*, Hilger and Watts Ltd., London 1964, p. 25.
131. GILBERT P. T.: *Anal. Chem.* **34**, 210 R (1962).
132. GINSBURG V. L., LIVSHIC D. M., SATARINA G. I.: *Zh. anal. khim.* **19**, 1089 (1964).
133. GINSBURG V. L., SATARINA G. I.: *Zav. lab.* **31**, 249 (1965).
134. GINSBURG V. L., SATARINA G. I.: *Zh. anal. khim.* **21**, 593 (1966).
135. GIRARD M. L., ROUSSELET F.: *Compt. Rendus* **260**, 1501 (1965).
136. GOLEB J. A., BRODY J. K.: *Anal. Chim. Acta* **28**, 457 (1963).
137. GOLEB J. A., YOKOYAMA Y.: *Anal. Chim. Acta* **30**, 213 (1964).
138. GOLEB J. A.: *Anal. Chim. Acta* **34**, 135 (1966).
139. GOLEB J. A.: *Anal. Chim. Acta* **36**, 130 (1966).
140. GÓMEZ COEDO A., JIMÉNEZ SECO J. L.: *Rev. metalurgia* **1**, 158 (1965).
141. GOODFELLOW G. I.: *Anal. Chim. Acta* **36**, 132 (1966).
142. GRAVES CH. C., BAHR D. W.: *NACA* Report 1300, p. 1 (1957).
143. GREAVES M. C.: *Nature* **199**, 552 (1963).
144. HAGENAH W. D., LAQUA K., MOSSOTTI V.: *Coll. Spec. Int.* **XII**. Exeter (1965).
145. HALLS D. J., TOWNSHEND A.: *Anal. Chim. Acta* **36**, 278 (1966).
146. HARRISON W. W.: *Anal. Chem.* **37**, 1168 (1965).
147. HEJTMÁNEK M., POLEJ B.: *Chem. listy* **60**, 532 (1966).
148. HENEAGE P.: *AAN* **5**, 64 (1966).
149. HERRMANN R., LANG W.: *Z. ges. experim. Med.* **134**, 268 (1961).
150. HERRMANN R.: *Optik* **18**, 422 (1961).
151. HERRMANN R., LANG W.: *Optik* **19**, 208 (1962).
152. HERRMANN R., LANG W.: *Z. ges. experim. Med.* **135**, 569 (1962).
153. HERRMANN R., LANG W.: *Arch. f. Eisenhüttenwesen* **33**, 643 (1962).
154. HERRMANN R., LANG W.: *Z. klin. Chem.* **1**, 182 (1962).
155. HERRMANN R., LANG W., RÜDIGER K.: *Z. anal. Chem.* **206**, 241 (1964).
156. HERRMANN R.: *Z. anal. Chem.* **212**, 1 (1965).
157. HERRMANN R., NEU W.: *Experimentia* **21**, 436 (1965).
158. HINNOV E., KOHN H.: *J. Opt. Soc. Am.* **47**, 156 (1957).
159. HINSON W. H.: *Spectrochim. Acta* **18**, 427 (1962).
160. HINSON W. H., KITCHING R.: *Spectrochim. Acta* **20**, 245 (1964).

161. HOPMAN F. W., KOHN H.: *J. Opt. Soc. Am.* **51**, 512 (1961).
162. HONEGGER N.: *Ärztl. Laboratorium* **2**, 41 (1963).
162A. HOOYMAYERS H. P., ALKEMADE C. T. J.: *J. Quant. Spectroscop. Radiat. Transfer* **6**, pp. 371, 847 (1966).
163. HORN D. B., LATNER A. L.: *Clinica chim. Acta* **8**, 974 (1963).
164. HUMPHREY J. R.: *Anal. Chem.* **37**, 1604 (1965).
165. HURST R. J., McSWINEY R. R.: *Hilger J.* **8**, 25 (1963).
166. IVANOV I. P., TALALAEV B. M.: *Zav lab.* **32**, 1481 (1966).
167. IVANOV N. P.: *Zhur. anal. khim.* **17**, 126 (1962).
168. IVANOV N. P., KOZYREVA N. A.: *Zav. lab.* **30**, 706 (1964).
169. IVANOV N. P., KOZYREVA N. A.: *Zh. anal. khim.* **19**, 1266 (1964).
170. IVANOV N. P., KOZYREVA N. A.: *Zavod. lab.* **31**, 566 (1965).
171. IVANOV N. P., GUSINSKIJ M. N., JESIKOV A. D.: *Zh. anal. khim.* **20**, 1133 (1965).
172. IVANOV N. P., MINERVINA L. V., BARANOV S. V., POFRALIDI L. G., OLIKOV I. I.: *Zh. anal. khim.* **21**, 1129 (1966).
173. JONES W. G., WALSH A.: *Spectrochim. Acta* **16**, 249 (1960).
174. JONES D. I. H., THOMAS T. A.: *Hilger J.* **9**, 39 (1965).
175. JOYNER T., FINLEY J. S.: *AAN* **5**, 4 (1966).
176. KAHN H. L., SLAVIN W.: *Appl. Optics* **2**, 931 (1963).
177. KAHN H. L.: *J. Chem. Ed.* **43**, A 7, A 103 (1966).
178. KEENAN R. G.: *J. Occup. Med.* **7**, 276 (1965).
179. KERBER J. D.: *Appl. Spectrosc.* **20**, 212 (1966).
180. KHALIFA H., SVEHLA G., ERDEY L.: *Acta Chim. Acad. Sci. Hung.* **41**, 187 (1964).
181. KHALIFA H., SVEHLA G., ERDEY L.: *Talanta* **12**, 703 (1965).
182. KINSON K., HODGES R. J., BELCHER C. B.: *Anal. Chim. Acta* **29**, 134 (1963).
183. KINSON K., BELCHER C. B.: *Anal. Chim. Acta* **30**, 64 (1964).
184. KINSON K., BELCHER B.: *Anal. Chim. Acta* **31**, 180 (1964).
185. KIRKBRIGHT G. F., PETERS M. K., WEST T. S.: *Analyst* **91**, 411 (1966).
186. KIRKBRIGHT G. F., SMITH A. M., WEST T. S.: *Analyst* **91**, 700 (1966).
187. KIRKBRIGHT G. F., PETERS M. K., WEST T. S.: *Analyst* **91**, 705 (1966).
188. KNISELEY R. N., D'SILVA A. P., FASSEL V. A.: *Anal. Chem.* **35**, 910 (1963).
189. KOIRTYOHANN S. R., FELDMAN C.: *Developments in Applied Spectroscopy* **3**, Ed. J. E. Forrette, E. Lanterman. Pienum Press 1964, N. Y.
190. KOIRTYOHANN S. R., PICKETT E. E.: *Anal. Chem.* **37**, 601 (1965).
191. KOIRTYOHANN S. R., PICKETT E. E.: *Anal. Chem.* **38**, 585 (1966).
192. KOIRTYOHANN S. R., PICKETT E. E.: *Anal. Chem.* **38**, 1087 (1966).
193. KOROVIN M. I., KUCHUMOV V. A., PRONIN I. S.: *Zav. lab.* **32**, 704 (1966).
194. LANG W., HERRMANN R.: *Optik* **19**, 422 (1962).
195. LANG W.: *Research theses*, Univ. Giessen (1963).
196. LANG W., HERRMANN R.: *Optik* **20**, 391 (1963).
197. LANG W., HERRMANN R.: *Optik* **20**, 347 (1963).
198. LANG W., HERRMANN R.: *Mikrochim. Acta* **1963**, 872.

199. LANG W., HERRMANN R.: *Mikrochim. Acta* **1963**, 1053.
200. LANG W., HERRMANN R.: *Z. anal. Chem.* **199**, 161 (1964).
201. LANG W.: *Mikrochim. Acta* **1964**, 796.
202. LANG W.: *Z. anal. Chem.* **217**, 161 (1966).
203. LANG W.: *Z. anal. Chem.* **219**, 321 (1966).
204. LEITHE W.: *Angew. Chem.* **73**, 488 (1961).
205. LEITHE W., HOFER A.: *Mikrochim. Acta* **1961**, 268.
206. LEITHE W.: *Mikrochim. Acta* **1961**, 277.
207. LOCKYER R.: *Hilger J.* **5**, 55 (1959).
208. LOCKYER R., HAMES G. E.: *Analyst* **84**, 385 (1959).
209. LOCKYER R., SCOTT J. E., SLADE S.: *Nature* **189**, 830 (1961).
210. LOCKYER R.: *Anal. Chem.*, Proc. Int. Sympos., Birmingham Univ. **1962**, 297 (1963).
211. LVOV B. V.: *Inzh. fiz. Zhur*, Minsk, **2**, 56 (1959).
212. LVOV B. V.: *Spectrochim. Acta* **17**, 761 (1961).
213. LVOV B. V.: *Zav. lab.* **28**, 931 (1962).
214. MAGEE R. J., RAHMAN A. K.: *Talanta* **12**, 409 (1965).
215. MALISSA H., SCHÖFFMANN E.: *Mikrochim. Acta* **1955**, 187.
216. MALMSTADT H. V., CHAMBERS W. E.: *Anal. Chem.* **32**, 225 (1960).
217. MANNING D. C., SLAVIN W.: *AAN* **8** (1962).
218. MANNING D. C.: *AAN* **24**, 6 (1964).
219. MANNING D. C., TRENT D. J., VOLLMER J.: *AAN* **4**, 234 (1965).
220. MANNING D. C., TRENT D. J., SPRAGUE J., SLAVIN W.: *AAN* **4**, 255 (1965).
221. MANNING D. C.: *AAN* **4**, 267 (1965).
222. MANNING D. C.: *AAN* **5**, 63 (1966).
223. MANNING D. C., CAPACHO-DELGADO L.: *Anal. Chim. Acta* **36**, 312 (1966).
223A. MANNING D. C.: *AAN* **5**, 127 (1966).
224. MANSELL R. E., EMMEL H. W.: *AAN* **4**, 365 (1965).
225. MANSELL R. E., EMMEL H. W., MCLAUGHLIN E. L.: *Appl. Spectrosc.* **20**, 231 (1966).
226. MANSFIELD J. M., WINEFORDMER J. D.: *Anal. Chem.* **37**, 1049 (1965).
226A. MARGOSHES M., DARR M. M.: *NBS*, Tech. Note **272**, 18 (1965).
227. MASSMAN H.: *Z. Instrumentenkunde* **71**, 225 (1963).
228. MASSMAN H.: *Coll. Spec. Int.* **XII**. Exeter (1965).
229. MAVRODINEANU R.,: *Spectrochim. Acta* **17**, 1016 (1961).
230. McBRIDE C. H.: *J. Assn. Official Agr. Chemistry* **48**, 406 and 1100 (1965).
231. McPHERSON G. L., PRICE J. W., SCAIFE P. H.: *Nature* **199**, 371 (1963).
232. McPHERSON G. L.: *AAN* **4**, 186 (1965).
233. MEANS E. A., RATCLIFF D.: *AAN* **4**, 174 (1965).
234. MENZIES A. C.: *Z. Instrumentenkunde* **68**, 242 (1960).
235. MENZIES A. C. *Anal. Chem.* **32**, 898 (1960)
236. MENZIES A. C.: *Optik aller Wellenlängen u. Spektroskopie*, Akad. Verlag, Berlin 1962, p. 566.

237. MESHKOVA S. B., POLUEKTOV N. S.: *Zh. prikl. spektroskopii* **2**, 21 (1965).
238. MESHKOVA S. B., ZELYUKOVA M. V., POLUEKTOV N. S.: *Zh. anal. khim.* **21**, 405 (1966).
239. MISLAN J. P.: At. Energy Ltd *AECL* **1941** (1964).
240. MISLAN J. P., MARK S. J.: *AECL* 2228 (Feb. 1965) — *CDRC* 1216.
241. MOORE E. J., MILNER O. I., GLASS J. R.: *Microchem. J.* **10**, 148 (1966).
242. MORGAN M. E.: *AAN* **21**, 1 (1964).
243. MOSER H., SCHULZ H.: *Ann. Physik* (7), **4**, 243 (1959).
244. MOSSOTTI V. G., FASSEL V. A.: *Spectrochim. Acta* **20**, 1117 (1964).
245. MOSTYN R. A., CUNNINGHAM A. F.: *Anal. Chem.* **38**, 121 (1966).
246. MULFORD C. E.: *ANN* **5**, 28 (1966).
247. MULFORD C. E.: *AAN* **5**, 63 (1966).
247A. MULFORD C. E.: *AAN* **5**, 88 (1966).
248. MURIE R. A., BOURKE R. C.: *Appl. Spectrosc.* **18**, 116 (1964).
249. NELSON L. S., KUEBLER N. A.: *Coll. Spec. Int.*, College Park, Maryland (1962).
250. NELSON L. S., KUEBLER N. A.: *Spectrochim. Acta* **19**, 781 (1963).
251. NESBITT R. W.: *Anal. Chim. Acta* **35**, 413 (1966).
252. NEWBURN E.: *Nature* **192**, 1182 (1961).
253. NIKOLAJEV G. I., ALESKOVSKIJ V. B.: *Zh. anal. khim.* **18**, 816 (1963).
254. NIKOLAJEV G. I.: *Zh. anal. khim.*, **19**, 63 (1964).
255. NIKOLAJEV G. I.: *Zh. anal. khim.* **20**, 445 (1965).
256. NORRIS J. A.: *Coll. Spec. Int.* **XII.** Exeter (1965).
257. OLSON A. M.: *AAN* **4**, 278 (1965).
258. OSBORN K. R., GUNNING H. E.: *J. Opt. Soc. Am.* **45**, 552 (1955).
259. PARKER H. E.: *AAN* **13**, 1 (1963).
260. PARSONS M. L., MCCARTHY W. J., WINFORDNER J. D.: *Appl. Spectrosc.* **20**, 223 (1966).
261. PASSMORE W., ADAMS P. B.: *AAN* **4**, 237 (1965).
262. PATASSY F. Z.: *Plant and Soil* **22**, 395 (1965).
263. PERKIN-ELMER Corp.: *Analytical Methods for Atomic Absorption Spectrophotometry* (1965).
264. PERKINS J.: *Analyst* **88**, 324 (1963).
265. PLATTE J. A., MARCY V. M.: *AAN* **4**, 289 (1965).
266. POLUEKTOV N. S., VITKUN R. A.: *Zh. anal. khim.* **16**, 260 (1961).
267. POLUEKTOV N. S., VITKUN R. A.: *Zh. anal. khim.* **17**, 935 (1962).
268. POLUEKTOV N. S., VITKUN R. A.: *Zh. anal. khim.* **18**, 37 (1963).
269. POLUEKTOV N. S., VITKUN R. A., ZELJUKOVA JU. V.: *Zh. anal. khim.* **19**, 937 (1964).
270. POSENER D. W.: *Austr. J. Physics* **12**, 184 (1959).
271. PRUGGER H.: *Optik* **21**, 320 (1964).
272. RAMAKRISHNA T. V., ROBINSON J. W., WEST P. W.: *Anal. Chim. Acta* **36**, 57 (1966).

272A. RAMAKRISHNA T. V., ROBINSON J. W., WEST P. W.: *Anal. Chim. Acta* **37**, 20 (1967).

273. RAMÍREZ-MUÑOZ: *Talanta* **13**, 87 (1966).

274. RAMÍREZ-MUÑOZ J., MALAKOFF J. L., AIME C. P.: *Anal. Chim. Acta* **36**, 328 (1966).

275. RANN C. S., HAMBLY A. N.: *Anal. Chim. Acta* **32**, 346 (1965).

276. RANN C. S., HAMBLY A. N.: *Anal. Chem.* **37**, 879 (1965).

277. RAWLING B. S., GREAVES M. C., AMOS M. P.: *Nature* **188**, 137 (1960).

278. RAZUMOV V. A., UTKINA T. P., AJDAROV T. K.: *Zh. anal. khim.* **20**, 1371 (1965).

279. ROBINSON J. W.: *Anal. Chim. Acta* **23**, 458 (1960).

280. ROBINSON J. W.: *Anal. Chim. Acta* **23**, 479 (1960).

281. ROBINSON J. W.: *Anal. Chim. Acta* **24**, 254 (1961).

282. ROBINSON J. W.: *Anal. Chim. Acta* **24**, 451 (1960).

283. ROBINSON J. W.: *Anal. Chem.* **33**, 1067 (1961).

284. ROBINSON J. W.: *Anal. Chim. Acta* **27**, 465 (1962).

285. ROBINSON J. W., KEVAN L. J.: *Anal. Chim. Acta* **28**, 170 (1963).

286. ROUSSELET F., GIRARD M. L.: *C. R. Acad. Sci.* **260**, 253 (1965).

287. RUBEŠKA I., MOLDAN B., VALNÝ Z.: *Anal. Chim. Acta* **29**, 206 (1963).

288. RUBEŠKA I.: *Chem. listy* **59**, 1119 (1965).

289. RUBEŠKA I., MOLDAN B.: *Acta Chim. Acad. Sci. Hung.* **44**, 367 (1965).

290. RUBEŠKA I., MOLDAN B.: *Collection* **30**, 1731–1735 (1965).

291. RUBEŠKA I., SVOBODA V.: *Anal. Chim. Acta* **32**, 253 (1965).

292. RUBEŠKA I., ŠTUPAR J.: *AAN* **5**, 69 (1966).

293. RUBEŠKA I., ŠULCEK Z., MOLDAN B.: *Anal. Chim. Acta* **37**, 27 (1967).

294. RUBEŠKA I., MOLDAN B.: *Anal. Chim. Acta* (1967).

294A. RUBEŠKA I., MOLDAN B.: *Unpublished results.*

294B. RUBEŠKA I.: *Anal. Chim. Acta* **40**, 187 (1968).

295. RUSSELL B. J., SHELTON J. P., WALSH A.: *Spectrochim. Acta* **8**, 317 (1957).

296. RUSSELL B. J., WALSH A.: *Spectrochim. Acta* **15**, 883 (1959).

297. SATTUR T. W.: *AAN* **5**, 37 (1966).

298. SCHULLER V. C. O., JAMES G. S.: *J.. S. Afr. Inst. Min. Metall.* **62**, 790 (1962).

299. SCHULLER V. C. O., JANSEN A. V., JAMES G. S.: *J. S. Afr. Inst. Min. Metall.* **62**, 807 (1962).

300. SEBENS C., VOLLMER J., SLAVIN W.: *AAN* **3**, 165 (1964).

301. SHIMAZU M., HASHIMOTO A.: *Science of Light* (Tokyo) **11**, 131 (1962).

302. SHAFTO R. G.: *AAN* **3**, 115 (1964).

303. SIMMONS E. C.: *AAN* **4**, 281 (1965).

304. SIMON L.: *Optik* **19**, 621 (1962).

305. SKEWES H. R.: *Austr. Inst. Min. Metall.* **211**, 217 (1964).

306. SKOGERBOE R. K., WOODRIFF R. A.: *Anal. Chem.* **35**, 1977 (1963).

307. SLAVIN W., MANNING D. C.: *Anal. Chem.* **35**, 253 (1963).

308. SLAVIN W., SPRAGUE S., MANNING D. C.: *AAN* **18**, 1 (1964).

309. SLAVIN W.: *AAN* **3**, 141 (1964).
310. SLAVIN W., TRENT D. J., SPRAGUE S.: *AAN* **4**, 180 (1965).
311. SLAVIN W., SEBENS C., SPRAGUE S.: *AAN* **4**, 341 (1965).
312. SLAVIN W.: *Appl. Spectrosc.* **19**, 32 (1965).
313. SLAVIN W., MANNING D. C.: *Appl. Spectrosc.* **19**, 65 (1965).
313A. SLAVIN W., VENGHIATTIS A., MANNING D. C.: *AAN* **5**, 84 (1966).
314. SPRAGUE S., SLAVIN W.: *AAN* **12** (1963); *AAN* **4**, 367 (1965).
315. SPRAGUE S., MANNING D. C., SLAVIN W.: *AAN* **20**, 1 (1964).
315A. SPRAGUE S., SLAVIN W.: *AAN* **23**, 8 (1964).
316. SPRAGUE S., SLAVIN W.: *AAN* **3**, 160 (1964).
317. SPRAGUE S., SLAVIN W.: *AAN* **4**, 228 (1965).
318. STEWART W. K., HUTCHINSON F., FLEMING L. W.: *J. Lab. and Chem. Med.* **61**, 858 (1963).
319. STRASHEIM A., STRELOW F. W. E., BUTLER L. R. P.: *J. S. Afr. Chem. Inst.* **13**, 73 (1960).
320. STRASHEIM A.: *Nature* **196**, 1194 (1962).
321. STRASHEIM A.: *Appl. Spectrosc.* **16**, 109 (1962).
322. STRASHEIM A., BUTLER L. R. P., MASKEW E. C.: *J. S. Afr. Inst. Min. Metall.* **62**, 796 (1962).
323. STRASHEIM A., WESSELS G. J.: *Appl. Spectrosc.* **17**, 65 (1963).
324. STRASHEIM A., NORVAL E., BUTLER L. R. P.: *J. S. Afr. Chem. Inst.* **17**, 55 (1964).
325. STRELOW F. W. E., FEAST E. C., MATHEWS P. M., BOTHMA C. J. C., VAN ZIL C. R.: *Analyt. Chem.* **38**, 115 (1966).
326. STUMPF K. E., GONSIOR T.: *Coll. Spec. Inst.* **IX**. Lyon (1961).
327. SULLIVAN J. V., WALSH A.: *Spectrochim. Acta* **21**, 721 (1965).
328. SULLIVAN J. V., WALSH A.: *Spectrochim. Acta* **21**, 727 (1965).
329. SUNDERMAN F. W.: *Am. J. Clin. Path.* **44**, 182 (1965).
330. SUNDERMAN F. W., CARROLL J. E.: *Am. J. Clin. Path.* **43**, 302 (1965).
331. SUZUKI M., YANAGISAWA M., TAKEUCHI T.: *Talanta* **12**, 989 (1965).
332. ŠTUPAR J.: *Z. anal. Chem.* **203**, 401 (1964).
333. ŠTUPAR J., PODOBNIK B., KOROŠIN J.: *Croatica Chemica Acta* **37**, 141 (1965).
334. ŠTUPAR J.: *Mikrochim. Acta* 722 (1966).
335. TAKEUCHI T., SUZUKI M.: *Talanta* **11**, 1391 (1964).
336. TAKEUCHI T., SUZUKI M., YANAGISAWA M.: *Anal. Chim. Acta* **36**, 258 (1966).
337. TARDON S., BALCÁRKOVÁ M.: *Chem. listy* **60**, 334 (1966).
338. TINDALL F. M.: *AAN* **4**, 339 (1965).
339. TOSHIMITSU MUSHA: *J. Physic. Soc. Japan* **17**, 1440 (1962).
340. TRENT D., SLAVIN W.: *AAN* **19** (1964); *AAN* **3**, 118 (1964).
341. TRENT D., SLAVIN W.: *AAN* **3**, 131 (1964).
342. TRENT D. J., MANNING D. C., SLAVIN W.: *AAN* **4**, 335 (1965).
343. TRENT D. J.: *AAN* **4**, 348 (1965).
344. VAUGHN W. W., MCCARTHY J. E.: *U. S. Geol. Survey*, Prof. Paper 501 D, pp. D123—D127 (1964).

345. VEILLON C., MANSFIELD J. M., PARSONS M. L., WINEFORDNER J. D.: *Anal. Chem.* **38**, 204 (1966).
346. VOLLMER J., SEBENS C., SLAVIN W.: *AAN* **4**, 306 (1965).
347. WALLACE F. J.: *Hilger J.* **7**, 39 (1962).
348. WALLACE F. J.: *Hilger J.* **7**, 65 (1963).
349. WALLACE F. J.: *Analyst* **88**, 259 (1963).
350. WALSH A.: *Spectrochim. Acta* **7**, 108 (1955).
351. WALSH A.: *Advances in Spectroscopy*, H. W. Thompson, ed., Interscience, New York (1961), Vol. II.
352. WALSH A.: *Coll. Spectroscop. Int.* **X** (1962), 127.
353. WALSH A.: *Anal. Chem.*, Proc. Int. Sympos., Birmingham Univ. **1962**, 281 (1963).
354. WALSH A.: *Coll. Spec. Int.* **XII.** Exeter (1965).
355. WENDT R. R., FASSEL V. A.: *Anal. Chem.* **37**, 920 (1965).
356. WENDT R. R., FASSEL V. A.: *Anal. Chem.* **38**, 337 (1966).
357. WILLIAMS C. H., DAVID D. J., IISMAAA O.: *J. Agric. Sci.* **59**, 388 (1962).
358. WILLIAMS J. B.: *Nature* **184**, 186 (1959).
359. WILLIS J. B.: *Spectrochim. Acta* **16**, 259 (1960).
360. WILLIS J. B.: *Spectrochim. Acta* **16**, 273 (1960).
361. WILLIS J. B.: *Spectrochim. Acta* **16**, 551 (1960).
362. WILLIS J. B.: *Anal. Chem.* **33**, 556 (1961).
363. WILLIS J. B.: *Proc. Roy. Austr. Chem. Inst.*, July, 245 (1962).
364. WILLIS J. B.: *Methods of Biochemical Analysis.* Interscience, New York (1962), vol. XI.
365. WILLIS J. B.: *Anal. Chem.* **34**, 614 (1962).
366. WILLIS J. B.: *Austr. J. Dairy Technol.*, June 1964.
367. WILLIS J. B.: *Nature* **207**, 715 (1965).
368. WILSON H. W.: *Anal. Chem.* **38**, 920 (1966).
369. WILSON L.: *Anal. Chim. Acta* **30**, 377 (1964).
370. WILSON L.: *Anal. Chim. Acta* **35**, 123 (1966).
371. WINEFORDNER J. D., LATZ H. W.: *Anal. Chem.* **33**, 1727 (1961).
372. WINEFORDNER J. D., MANSFIELD C. T., VICKERS T. J.: *Anal. Chem.* **35**, 1611 (1963).
373. WINEFORDNER J. D., MANSFIELD C. T., VICKERS T. J.: *Anal. Chem.* **35**, 1607 (1963).
374. WINEFORDNER J. D.: *Appl. Spectrosc.* **17**, 109 (1963).
375. WINEFORDNER J. D., VICKERS T. J.: *Anal. Chem.* **36**, 161 (1964).
376. WINEFORDNER J. D., STAAB R. A.: *Anal. Chem.* **36**, 165 (1964).
377. WINEFORDNER J. D., STAAB R. A.: *Anal. Chem.* **36**, 1367 (1964).
378. WINEFORDNER J. D., VICKERS T. J.: *Anal. Chem.* **36**, 1939 (1964).
379. WINEFORDNER J. D., VICKERS T. J.: *Anal. Chem.* **36**, 1947 (1964).
380. WINEFORDNER J. D., VEILLON C.: *Anal. Chem.* **37**, 416 (1965).
381. WOODSON T. T.: *Rev. Sci. Instrum.* **10**, 308 (1939).

382. WÜNSCH A., TEICHER K.: *Z. Pflanzenernähr. Düngemittel* **97**, 101 (1962).
383. YASUDA K.: *Anal. Chem.* **38**, 592 (1966).
384. ZAJDLE A. N., *Opt. i spektroskopija* **4**, 701, (1958).
385. ZAJDLE A. N., KORENNOJ E. P.: *Opt. i spektroskopija* **10**, 570 (1961).
386. ZAJDLE A. N., KORENNOJ E. P.: *Zav. lab.* **29**, 1449 (1963).
387. ZALUBAS R., WILSON M.: *J. Res. Natl. Bur. Std.* A **69**, 59 (1965).
388. ZAUGG W. S., KNOX R. J.: *Anal. Chem.* **38**, 1759 (1966).
389. ZEEMAN P. B., BUTLER L. R. P.: *Appl. Spectrosc.* **16**, 120 (1962).
390. ZELJUKOVA JU. V., POLUEKTOV N. S.: *Zh. anal. khim.* **18**, 435 (1963).
391. ZELJUKOVA JU, V., NIKONOVA M. P., POLUEKTOV N. S.: *Zh. anal. khim.* **21**, 1409 (1966).
392. ZETTNER A., SELIGSON D.: *Clin. Chem.* **10**, 869 (1964).
393. ZETTNER A., MANSBACH L.: *Am. J. Clin. Path.* **44**, 517 (1965).
394. ZHITKEVICH V. F., LJUTYJ A. I., NESTERKO N. A., ROSSICHIN V. S., CIKORA I. L.: *Izv. vyssh. ucheb. zaved.* Fizika **1963**, 78.
395. ZHITKEVICH V. F., LJUTYJ A. I., NESTERKO N. A., ROSSICHIN V. S., CIKORA I. L.: *Opt. i spektroskopija* **14**, 35 (1963).

AAN = Atomic Absorption, Newsletter, Perkin-Elmer Corp., Norwalk, Connecticut, U.S.A.

Literature

(Recently published papers)

396. ADAMSON C. V.: *Anal. Chem.* **35**.
397. ARMENTROUT D.: *Anal. Chem.* **38**, 1235 (1966).
398. BOWMAN J. A.: *Anal. Chim. Acta* **37**, 465 (1967).
399. BROOKS R. R., PRESLEY B. J., KAPLAN I. R.: *Talanta* **14**, 809 (1967).
400. BURRELL D. C.: *Anal. Chim. Acta* **38**, 447 (1967).
401. DAGNALL R. M., THOMPSON K. C., WEST T. S.: *Talanta* **14**, 551 (1967).
402. DAGNALL R. M., THOMPSON K. C., WEST T. S.: *Talanta* **14**, 557 (1967).
403. FELDMAN F. J., KNOBLOCH E. C., PURDY W. C.: *Anal. Chim. Acta* **38**, 489 (1967).
404. FRANK G. W., SCHRENK W. G., MELOAN C. E.: *Anal. Chem.* **39**, 534 (1967).
405. GALAN L. DE, MCGEE W. W., WINEFORDNER J. D.: *Anal. Chim. Acta* **37**, 436 (1967).
406. GOODFELLOW G. I.: *Appl. Spectrosc.* **21**, 39 (1967).
407. HEADRIDGE J. B., HUBBARD D. P.: *Anal. Chim. Acta* **37**, 151 (1967).
408. IVANOV N. P., TALALAEV B. M.: *Zh. anal. khim.* **22**, 634 (1967).
409. JAWOROWSKI R. J., WEBERLING R. P., BRACO D. J.: *Anal. Chim. Acta* **37**, 284 (1967).
410. KINNUNEN J., LINDSJÖ O.: *Chemist-Analyst* **56**, 25 (1967).

411. KIRKBRIGHT G. F., PETERS M. K., WEST T. S.: *Talanta* **14**, 789 (1967).
412. KIRKBRIGHT G. F., SEMB A., WEST T. S.: *Talanta* **14**, 1011 (1967).
413. KOLB B., KEMMNER G., SCHLESER F. H., WIEDEKING E.: *Z. anal. Chem.* **221**, 166 (1966).
414. LANG W.: *Z. anal. Chem.* **223**, 241 (1967).
415. MANNING D. C.: *AAN* **6**, 35 (1967).
416. MANNING D. C., VOLLMER J.: *AAN* **6**, 38 (1967).
417. MARSHALL D., SCHRENK W. G.: *Appl. Spectrosc.* **21**, 246 (1967).
418. MARSHALL G. B., WEST Z. S.: *Talanta* **14**, 823 (1967).
419. MASSMANN H.: *Chimia* **21**, 217 (1967).
420. MASSMANN H.: *Z. anal. Chem.* **225**, 203 (1967).
421. MCGEE W. W., WINEFORDNER J. D.: *Anal. Chim. Acta* **37**, 429 (1967).
422. MEDDINGS B., KAISER H.: *AAN* **6**, 28 (1967).
423. MOSTYN R. A., CUNNINGHAM A. F.: *Anal. Chem.* **39**, 433 (1967).
424. RAMAKRISHNA T. V., WEST P. W., ROBINSON J. W.: *Analyst* **39**, 81 (1967).
425. SACHDEV S. L., ROBINSON J. W., WEST P. W.: *Anal. Chim. Acta* **37**, 12 (1967).
426. SACHDEV S. L., ROBINSON J. W., WEST P. W.: *Anal. Chim. Aeta* **37**, 156 (1967).
427. SACHDEV S. L., ROBINSON J. W., WEST P. W.: *Anal. Chim. Acta* **38**, 499 (1967).
428. SCHRENK W. G., LEHMAN D. A., NEUFELD L.: *Appl. Spectrosc.* **20**, 389 (1966).
429. SULLIVAN J. V., WALSH A.: *Spectrochim. Acta* **22**, 1843 (1966).
430. TASKAEVA T. P., VAJNSHTEJN E. N.: *Zh. anal. khim.* **22**, 852 (1967).
431. THILLIEZ G.: *Anal. Chem.* **39**, 427 (1967).
432. VEENENDAAL W. A., POLAK H. L.: *Z. anal. Chem.* **223**, 17 (1967).
433. WEIR D. R., KOFLUK R. P.: *AAN* **6**, 24 (1967).
434. WILSON H. W.: *Anal. Chem.* **38**, 920 (1966).
435. WINEFORDNER J. D., PARSONS M. L., MANSFIELD J. M., MCCARTHY W. J.: *Anal. Chem.* **39**, 436 (1967).
436. ZELJUKOVA JU. V., POLUEKTOV N. S., NIKONOVA M. P.: *Zav. lab.* **33**, 436 (1967).
437. ZOLOTOV JU. A., KUZMIN N. M.: *Zh. anal. khim.* **22**, 773 (1967).

INDEX

Absorbance, 21, 84
  relation with atomic concentration, 22–26
  experimental evaluation of, 92–95
Absorption, atomic, 13–27
  non-selective, 101–2
Absorption coefficient, atomic, 15–17
Absorption flame photometry, defined, 11
Absorption law (Beer–Lambert), 21–22, 82, 92
Absorption oscillator strength, expression for, 14
Absorption tubes, construction and uses 43–48
Acetylene–air flame, 82
  constituents of, 42
Acetylene–nitrous oxide flame, 123, 140, 151, 154, 169
  emission spectrum of, 152
Acetylene–oxidant fuel mixtures, 31, 32
  burner for, 34
Acetylene–oxygen flame, 42
Aerosol, 32, 101–2
  dispersal in flame, 37–38
Air, 10, 135
Air–fuel mixtures, 31
Alloy(s)
  non-ferrous, 148
  steel, 143
Aluminium, 49, 151, 169

alloys, 120, 130, 148
optimum line for, 96
Ammonium pyrrolidin dithiocarbamate (ADPC), 127, 128
Antimony, 138, 169
Arsenic, 150–1, 169
Atomic vapours, production of, 29–50
Atomisation yield, 35
  for total consumption burners, 37
Atomiser, 32
  pneumatic, construction of, 36
    for sample transport into flame, 35

Barium, 176
Beer, 148
Beer–Lambert law, 21–22, 82, 92
Bending of analytical curves, 24, 25, 100
Beryllium, 151, 169
Biological materials, 120, 129, 143, 169
Bismuth, 130, 138, 169
Blocking effects, 98, 99, 151
Blood, 129
Blood plasma, 120
Blood serum, 113, 120, 122, 124, 128, 129, 148
Boltzmann equation, 26, 96
Boron, 151, 169
Brain tissue, 120, 129
Brass, 130
Brines, 148
  oil-field, 113, 120

Broadening of absorption lines, 19
    due to Doppler effect, 31
Buffering agents, 99, 112, 142, 145
Burners, 32–35
    background noise, elimination of, 35
    clogging defects, 30, 34
    fuel–oxidant mixtures for, 31
    of glass, 34
    heads, constructional materials for, 34
    laminar flow type, 33, 34
    of plastics, 34
    slot type, 34
    streaming velocity of gas mixture
        through, 30
    total consumption type, 33, 35
Burning velocity, 31
Butter oil, 129

Cadmium, 130, 135, 169
Caesium, 117
Calcium, 113, 120, 123–5, 129
Calcium oxide aerosol, 38
Catalysts, 143
Cathode sputtering chamber, 50, 54,
    155
Cement, 120, 148
Chelating agents, 119, 123, 127, 139
    elements forming, and pH range for,
        128
Chloroplasts, 120, 129
Chromium, 142–3, 145, 169
Cloud chamber, 32, 36
    conditions for acetylene–oxygen–
        nitrogen fuels, 34
    for oxygen fuel, 30
    droplet separation from fine mist in,
        35
    flow spoilers in, 36
Coal, 120
Coal ash, 126
Coal gas–air fuel mixtures, 31, 32
Cobalt, 25, 141–3, 147–9, 170
Copper, 130, 132

Copper alloys, 148
Cracking feedstocks, 143
Cyanogen–oxidant fuel mixture, 31

Dark current through photomultiplier,
    69
Depressive effects of ions, 118, 137
    phosphate ions, 122, 123, 135
Detection limits of elements, 81–83,
    104–5, 153, 157
Detectors, photoelectric, 68, 83, 170
Dissociation constants, derivation of,
    39–42
    alkali metal halides, 110
Doppler line width, 19, 20
Doppler-shaped lines, bending of, 24
Dysprosium, 153

Effective absorption coefficient, 22–23
Electric arc, for vapour production, 48
Electric dipole oscillator, 14
Electrodeless discharge tubes, high fre-
    quency, 62−63
    microwave frequency, 63, 150
Emission oscillator strength, 15
Energy levels, transition between, 13
Erbium, 153
Evaporation of aerosols in flame, 37–39
Excited state, atoms in, 13, 16, 19, 26, 27

Faeces, 143
Fertilisers, 142, 148
Filters, 65
Flame, 63
    chemical types, 29
    constituents of different types, 42
    dissociation and ionisation reactions
        in, 39–43
    evaporation of solvents in, 37–39
    premixed type, 30
    red feather zone in, 152, 169
    transport of sample into, 35−37
Flame noise, 35, 82–83, 170

Flame photometry, 30, 106
  absorption, 11
    flame mixtures used in. 30 – 32
    organic solvents in, 170
  emission, 7, 10
  scheme of physical and chemical processes occurring in, 97, 98
Flame temperature of fuel–oxidant mixtures, 31
Flash back danger, 30, 32, 35
Flow spoilers, in cloud chambers, 36
Fluorescence spectrometry, atomic, 155–8
  detection limits attained by, 157
Fluorescent radiation energy, 28
Fuel–oxidant mixtures, 31

Gadolinium, 153
Gallium, 149 – 50
Gasoline, 129, 130, 137, 169
Gaussian profiles, 20, 24
Germanium, 151, 169
Glass, 120, 130
Gold, 130, 139, 140, 143, 148
Graphite furnace, 48, 155, 169
Gratings, diffraction, resolving power of, 67

Hafnium, 151
Half–width, 18
  of lines in acetylene–air flame, 20
Hollow-cathode lamps, 12, 51 – 54
  choice of filler gas for, 55 – 56, 58, 132
  graphite, 50
  high-brightness type, electrode assembly, 56
    uses, 142, 154
  laboratory-made, 58 – 60
  operation of, 57 – 58
  radiation flux density, 54 – 56
  spectral line widths emitted from, 24
  water-cooled demountable, 50
  with shielded cathodes, 170

Holmium, 153
Hydrocarbon flame, reaction zone, 30
Hydrocarbon oils, 144, 154 (*See also* Cracking feedstocks, Gasoline, Lubricating oils)
Hydrogen–air flame, 82
  constituents of, 42
Hydrogen–air fuel mixtures, 31, 32
Hydrogen lamps, 64
Hydrogen–oxygen flame, 42
Hydrogen peroxide, 130

Ignition temperatures of fuel–oxidant mixtures, 31
Impact broadening, 19
Indium, 149
Interference effects, 97–100
  ionization, 32, 115, 116, 117, 121
Ionisation constants, derivation of, 39–42
  of alkali metal chlorides, 111
Ionisation energy of elements, 159–68
Iridium, 139, 141, 149–50
Iron, 25, 75, 120, 130, 141–4, 147, 170
  cast iron, 123, 148

Ketone solvents, 127, 128
King's furnace, 11
Kirchhoff's law, 9

Laminar flame, 30
  burners, 33, 34
Lanthanum, 153, 154
  as releasing agent, 119, 123, 142
Laser pulse, 53
Lead, 129, 136, 169
Light scatter by aerosol particles, 101–2
Limestone, 113, 120
Line, analytical, choice of, 95–6, 159–68
Line profile, absorption, defined, 17
Line width, defined, 18
Lithium, isotopic analysis, 53, 64, 113–15
  ionisation constant, 111

Lorentz broadening, 19
Lubricating oils, 144, 148
Lutecium, 153
Lvov furnace, 48, 155

Magnesium, 113, 118, 120, 121, 123, 129
    atoms in excited state in, 27
Manganese, 129, 142–3, 146–7, 170
Measuring systems, modulated, 72–3
"Memory" effect in absorption tubes,
    47
Mercury, 10, 129, 135
Methyl isobutyl ketone (MIBK), 127
Milk, 129
Molybdenum, 142, 145–6
Monochromators, 66–68
    resonance detector, 76–77
    selective modulators, 75
    slit function, 65, 66–68

Nanometer, defined, 27
Nebuliser, 32
Neodydinium, 153
Nickel, 25, 141–4, 149, 170
    determination by selective modulation
        method, 76
Nickel alloys, 120, 143
Nickel-plating solutions, 130, 144
Niobium, 131, 151, 169
Nitric oxide, 151
    –acetylene fuel mixture, 31, 32
Nitrous oxide, 151
    –acetylene flame, 123, 140, 152–4
    –acetylene fuel mixtures, 31, 32

Optical depth, 23
Ores, 130, 148
Oscillator strength of atoms, 9, 13
    line of greatest, 95–96
    of lines of main elements, 159–68
Osmium, 141
Oxine, 123

Palladium, 130, 139, 140
Parasite radiation, 25, 84–85
    elimination of unabsorbed, 100
Phosphates, 143
    depressive effects of, 122, 123, 135
Photometric errors, 84–85
Photomultipliers, 68–70
    scale expansion, 71–72
Plants, 113, 120, 129, 143
Plasma jets, 49–50
Platinum, 139, 141
Potassium, 113, 116
    atoms in excited state in, 26
Precision, 84, 86
    coefficients for calculating confidence
        limits, 87
    in routine analysis, 170
Pressure broadening, 19
Prism, resolving power of, 67
Profile function, 18
Propane–air fuel mixtures, 31, 32

Quantum efficient coefficient, defined,
    158

Radiation, density of, defined, 13
    emitted by thermally excited atoms,
        27
    isolation and detection of, 65–70
Radiation flux density (J), 15
    measurement of, 21–22
Rare earth elements, 151, 153, 169
Reactor coolant, 143
Recorder trace, 93
Releasing agents, 119, 124, 142
Resonance broadening, 19, 25
Resonance detector, 77
Resonance fluorescence, atomic, 27–28
Rhenium, 151, 169
Rhodium, 130, 139, 141
Rocks or minerals, 113, 123, 125, 126,
    148
Rubidium, 113, 116

Saliva, 120
Samarium, 153
Scale expansion, 71, 84, 93, 94
Scandium, 151
Sea water, 113, 129, 143, 148
Selective modulators, 75
Selenium. 103, 150–1
Sensitivities, 159–68
   absolute and relative, 80
   of commercial models, 104–5, 153
Silica tubes, 44–46
Silicate rocks, 120, 169
Silicon, 151
Silver, 131, 133
Skin effect, 63
Sodium, 113, 115, 148
   ionisation constant, 111
Soils, 113, 120, 129
Solvents, organic, 127
   APDC–MIBK system, 149, 170
   effect, 99
   evaporation in flame, 37
Spectral absorption coefficient, 21
Spectral lines. See under Line
Spectral interferences, 97, 100
Spectrograph, resolving power of, 68
Spectrophotometers, 10
   commercial models, 11, 104
      double beam instrument, 73–75, 93
      sensitivities of, 32, 104, 153
   operation of, 88–90
Spray chamber, 33
Standard addition method, 94–95
Standard solutions of elements, 90–92
   suitable for pneumatic atomisers,
      36–37
Steel, 123, 130, 142–3, 148
   stainless, 130
Strontium, 120, 125–6
   as releasing agent, 119, 123, 142
Sulphide ores, 148

Tantalum, 131, 151
Tellurium, 150–1
Terbium, 153
Thallium, 149–50, 169
Thermal excitation of free atoms,
   26–27
Thorium, 151
Tin, 130, 136
Titanium, 151, 169
Trace elements, standard solutions of,
   90–91
Transportation interference effects, 97
Tungsten, 151
Tungsten carbide, 144
Tungsten iodide lamps, 64

Uranium, 120, 151
Uranium compounds, 135
Urine, 120, 125, 129, 137, 148

Vanadium, 151, 154
Vapour discharge lamps, 60–62
   emission of energy in the resonance
      doublet, 65
   use for determining alkali metals, 112
Voigt profile, 20

Water, 113, 143, 148
Wavelengths of lines used, 159–68
Wines, 129

Xenon lamps, 64, 170

Ytterbium, 153
Yttrium, 151

Zinc, 49, 129, 134, 169
   atoms in excited state in, 27
Zirconium, 151